Helicopters and Autogiros

AIRMEN & AIRCRAFT

Martin Caidin, General Edi[tor]

Also:

Helicopters

and

Autogiros

A Chronicle of Rotating-wing Aircraft

by Charles Gablehouse

J. B. LIPPINCOTT COMPANY

Philadelphia and New York

Copyright © 1967 by Charles Gablehouse
Second Printing
Printed in the United States of America
LIBRARY OF CONGRESS CATALOG CARD NUMBER 66-18444

To Marge

Preface

THE FIRST THREE CHAPTERS of this book trace the complex and fascinating history of the helicopter from ancient times to the present day. The chapters that follow thereafter describe its various uses and deal with aerodynamic and technical considerations as well. Although the book has been written primarily about aircraft that fall within the "rotating-wing" classification (helicopters and Autogiros), one chapter outlines other vertical and short take-off machines, particularly those types which are intended to supplant the helicopter.

Concerning the technical and theoretical explanations, I have tried to communicate the important ideas in plain language, including a basic explanation of the theory of flight and of rotor system design. To this end, whenever a new concept is introduced an explanation is furnished at that point in the text. The use of those possibly exasperating abbreviations such as "rpm" and "hp" has been avoided; these are always spelled out.

Technical developments notwithstanding, the history of the helicopter is a very human story as well, and my intention has been to tell both, weaving together a single broad narrative. I have tried to convey, for example, the enthusiasm of the early experimenters and the inherent drama of the many rescue operations in which helicopters have played such a prominent role.

Finally, in tribute to all the rotating-wing pioneers there is a quotation attributed to the eighteenth-century philosopher, Dr. Samuel Johnson, which seems particularly appropriate: "The power of Invention is conferred by nature upon the few, but the labor of working out the Science of an Invention is more than can be easily endured."

C.G.

Acknowledgments

THIS BOOK would have been impossible without the encouragement and assistance of many persons and organizations in the aviation industry. First, I wish to express my great appreciation to D. H. Kaplan of Convertawings, Inc., who furnished the source material for the chapter on rotor design and patiently reviewed the rest of the manuscript as well. I also wish to thank Eugene K. Liberatore, who furnished important reference material and photos. Thanks are also in order for Ralph B. Lightfoot, Chief Engineer, Sikorsky Aircraft, for his assistance, and to New York Airways for its review of the material which describes the helicopter airlines. And I am particularly indebted to Harry M. Lounsbury, Executive Secretary of the American Helicopter Society and editor of its magazine *Verti-Flite*, who offered many helpful suggestions, and to E. Burke Wilford as well for his valuable assistance.

Another important contribution was from Maurice Claisse of the French firm, Société Breguet, the test pilot for the Breguet helicopter of 1935, who generously furnished photos and a description of those historic flights. I am also grateful for the photos and material on Soviet aircraft furnished by Ralph P. Alex of Sikorsky Aircraft and for the invaluable assistance provided by Chet Withington of Sikorsky; the extensive historical research and material from Lieutenant Colonel C. V. Glines, Chief of the Pentagon's Magazine and Book

Branch; and equally important contributions from George E. Brown of the Hiller Aircraft Company, Weston B. Haskell, Jr., of the Kaman Aircraft Corporation, J. H. Orpen and William L. Thomas of the Bell Helicopter Company; Eugene DuBois of Eastern Air Lines; Floyd R. Brown of the Aircraft Division of the Hughes Tool Company; William L. Thomas, editor of the *Lockheed-Georgia Quarterly;* N. L. Mead of the Curtiss-Wright Corporation; Mark E. Nevils of the Boeing Company, George J. Becker, Jr., of the Ryan Aeronautical Company . . . and for the assistance of many, many others in the industry.

I also wish to express my appreciation to M. J. Randleman of the National Aeronautic Association (the N.A.A. is the United States representative of the Fédération Aeronautique Internationale), who provided much vital information on international helicopter records, and to Billy Parker of Bartlesville, Oklahoma, for the material he furnished on the early rotary engines.

To the following go the author's thanks for their cooperation and for permission to quote from published material: the Controller of Her Brittanic Majesty's Stationery Office for the extracts and illustrations from *British Intelligence Objectives Sub-Committee Overall Report No. 8, Rotating Wing Activities in Germany During the Period 1939-45,* London, 1948; to Duell, Sloan & Pearce, Inc., for quotations from *Straight Up: The Story of Vertical Flight* by Richard G. Hubler, Copyright 1961; to Max Parrish & Company, Ltd., London, for quotations from *Sir George Cayley* by J. Laurence Pritchard, and to Horizon Press (the United States publisher) as well for these quotations, reprinted by permission of the publisher, Horizon Press, from *Sir George Cayley* by J. Laurence Pritchard, Copyright 1961; to the Air Rescue Service (MATS), United States Air Force, for quotations from *A History of the Air Rescue Service* by John L. Vandegrift, printed by the Rollins Press, Inc., Florida, 1959; to Guy Michelet for a quotation from his book *Breguet,* Copyright 1963, Editions France-Empire, Paris; to Air Force ROTC, Air University, U.S. Air Force, Maxwell Air Force Base, Alabama, for material from *Foundations of Air Power,* 1958; to *The New York Times* for quotes from an editorial of July 9,

1963, ©1963 by The New York Times Company, reprinted by permission; to Sikorsky Aircraft, Division of United Aircraft Corporation, Stratford, Connecticut, for material from various issues of *The Bee-Hive, Sikorsky News,* and other Sikorsky publications; to Ralph P. Alex and the American Helicopter Society for the quotation on VTOL development which appeared in the July, 1959, issue of the *AHS Journal;* to the Hiller Aircraft Company, Inc. (a subsidiary of Fairchild Hiller), Palo Alto, California, for material from *One Way Up* by John F. Straubel, Copyright 1964, Hiller Aircraft Company, Inc.; to the Kaman Aircraft Corporation, Bloomfield, Connecticut, for quotations from Captain John C. Armstrong's description of a rescue operation which appeared in the December, 1961 issue of *Kaman Rotor Tips;* to *Business/Commercial Aviation Magazine,* a Ziff-Davis publication, New York, for permission to use material, written by the author of this book, which appeared in its August, 1962, issue; to *American Aviation* magazine, Washington, D.C., for portions of an article which appeared in its July, 1963, issue; to *Flying* magazine, Ziff-Davis Publishing Co., New York, for furnishing a number of historical photos; to *The Aeroplane and Commercial Aviation News,* Temple Press, Ltd., London, for permission to use an illustration which appeared in that magazine in 1934.

All quotations are from published sources noted here, in the Bibliography, or from material furnished by the person quoted and intended for publication in this book.

The source for the quotation in the Preface attributed to Dr. Samuel Johnson is "Proceedings, First Convertible Aircraft Congress, Philadelphia, Pa., 1949," sponsored by the American Helicopter Society and the Institute of the Aeronautical Sciences. Dr. Johnson's statement is mentioned in the foreword to the 1949 proceedings, written by E. Burke Wilford.

This book is not intended in any way to represent or reflect the viewpoint or opinions of any employer of the author, past or present.

Contents

Ezekiel saw the wheel,
'Way up in the middle of the air.
The big wheel move by faith;
The little wheel move by the grace of God;
A wheel in a wheel,
'Way in the middle of the air. . . .
                    —OLDTIME SPIRITUAL

Helicopters and Autogiros

I

The Dream:
Flying Machines Are Possible

Experiment! Experiment! . . . Flying Machines are possible so that a man may sit in the middle of them turning some device by which artificial wings may beat the Air!
—ROGER BACON (1214-1294)

THE ORIGIN of the helicopter might be traced back to the ancient Chinese, whose "flying tops" were recorded as early as the fourth century B.C. These tiny devices consisted of a short round stick with feathers mounted on top, resembling the blades of a modern propeller. Children could spin the stick with a string—in the same fashion as a regular top—or by rubbing it back and forth in their hands. The feathers were twisted slightly so they would strike the air at a small angle; as the stick turned, a lifting force was created and straight up went the top accompanied, no doubt, by the gleeful laughter of tiny Mandarins. Today, the flying top is still manufactured for children, usually in plastic. Perhaps ironically, this plaything is now almost always disguised as a toy helicopter.

Within the framework of western science, the helicopter has other beginnings. Although there is no record that he ever dealt directly with the problem of mechanical flight, that extraordinary Greek mathematician, physicist, and inventor, Archimedes of Syracuse, who lived and worked in the second century B.C., must be given credit for the first step. Archimedes is regarded as having perfected the principle of the rotating screw—same screw thread found on any common nut or bolt—for use as a water pump in draining sunken ships. In his pump, a continuous screw or helix was rotated inside a cylinder. Two things happened: first, the desired effect—the screw pushed against the water, thus moving it along. But not unnaturally there was another reaction as well: the water resisted this pressure and pushed back. Many centuries later this second phenomenon was adapted to the movement of screwlike surfaces through a different fluid—air.

After the decline of the ancient civilizations, well over a thousand years passed before further progress was recorded. In the thirteenth century, with the reawakening of western science, the great English natural philosopher Roger Bacon turned to the possibilities of mechanical flight. He may have been the first to crystallize the idea of men building machines that could fly. The first translation, in 1597, into Elizabethan English of his *The Secrets of Art and Nature* has a passage which mentions "yea instruments to fly withall . . . by which the wings being artificially composed may beate the ayre after the manner of a flying bird." Bacon's approach to all science marked a turning point in human history; he insisted that nothing be accepted as fact unless it had been proved by actual experiments.

Two centuries passed, and another universal genius in the tradition of Archimedes and Bacon, the Italian artist-engineer Leonardo da Vinci, proposed nothing less than the full-blown concept of the helicopter. Struggling with the enigma of flight, he sketched designs for wing-flapping gliders, parachutes, and man-carrying airscrews that were the ancestors of today's helicopter. Da Vinci comprehended an elemental truth, that water and air are both fluids. In his writings he compared the movement of bodies of water to that of the wind and commented that the flight of a bird resembled the swimming of a fish through water. From this he proceeded to the thought that the Archimedean screw, meant to push along a flow of water, might work in air as well if it were turned fast enough, except that now the useful result would be obtained from the resistance of the fluid—the air would fight back and try to lift the screw—and thus a flying machine could be created. In describing his airscrew, Da Vinci wrote: "I find that if this instrument with a screw be well made—that is to say, made of linen of which the pores be stopped up with starch—and be turned swiftly, the said screw will make its spiral in the air and it will rise high." Later, in a key passage, he came to grips with the basic principle when he wrote that "when force generates swifter movement than the flight of the unresisting air, this air becomes compressed after the manner of feathers compressed and crushed by the weight of a sleeper. And the thing which drove the air, finding resistance in it, rebounds after the manner of a ball struck against a wall."

Among the hundreds of sketches made by Da Vinci, there is a lifting airscrew—the instrument referred to in his copious notes, written in a secret backhand script. We have no way of knowing whether a model was ever constructed of this sketch, made in 1483. Nevertheless, to Da Vinci belongs the credit for the vision of a man flying by means of an airscrew, though almost three centuries would pass before the first working models—of which we have any record—were constructed.

The very first self-propelled model of a lifting airscrew seems to have been the spring-driven device constructed and flown by a Russian, Mikhail V. Lomonosov, in 1754. Lomonosov, the "Father of Russian Science," was a pioneer physicist, chemist, astronomer, geologist, and geographer as well as a researcher in aeronautics—another universal genius intrigued with the dream of helicopter flight. In July, 1754, he demonstrated his model to the Russian Academy of Sciences. The proceedings of the Academy had this to say of the device, which the scientist intended for use in lifting thermometers and other small instruments into the air: "The honorable Advisor Lomonosov demonstrated his invention called *Aerodynamic* to be used for the purpose of depressing the air by means of wings rotated horizontally in the opposite directions by the agency of a spring of the type used in clocks in order to lift the machine into the upper layers of the air." It appears that, during the course of this demonstration, the model was not actually in free flight but was suspended from a string.

In 1768 the French mathematician J. P. Paucton published a treatise, *Théorie de la vis d'Archimedes,* in which he described a man-powered flying machine which had two airscrews. The apparatus, which he called a "Ptérophere," had one airscrew to support the machine in flight and a second to provide forward propulsion. However impractical, Paucton's proposal seems to have been the first in Europe which put forth the helicopter principle for a man-carrying aircraft.

The earliest working model in Europe was constructed by two Frenchmen, a naturalist named Launoy and a skilled mechanic, Bienvenu, who combined their talents to produce a tiny spring-driven helicopter, in principle resembling the model flown by Lomonosov. Like the Russian's, it had been designed with two rotors driven by a spring, on a single shaft, with the rotors turning in opposite directions. This feature was important—it solved the problem of *torque,* the tendency of the shaft of a single-rotor model to twist in the direction opposite to that in which the rotor was turning. With the two rotors turning in opposite directions, these forces canceled out. The rotor blades were made of feathers. Demonstrated in 1784 before the French Academy of Sciences, the tiny model was flown in free flight and rose to a respectable height with its feather rotors whirring away. Interest in the experiment was widespread and attracted the attention of scientists through Europe.

After Launoy and Bienvenu, the next important figure in rotating-wing history is an Englishman, Sir George Cayley. A baronet whose estates were at Brampton in Yorkshire, Cayley was born in 1773 and lived until 1857. A remarkable "amateur" scientist, engineer and experimenter, his interests were so broad and far-ranging that it is difficult, if not impossible, to categorize him. He played an active role in the growth of British engineering during the crucial first half of the eighteenth century, but he was also a member of Parliament, a writer, and a reformer active in the struggle to abolish Negro slavery. His interests included such diverse and unlikely fields as the design of theaters, theoretical aeronautics, the rights of labor, the

1. The Father of Aerial Navigation: Sir George Cayley, English scientist, engineer, Member of Parliament, born 1773, died 1857, is recognized as the originator of heavier-than-air flight. His aeronautical experiments date from the 1790's, and his writings show a clear understanding of the basic principles of airplane and helicopter flight. Painting is by Henry Perronet Briggs.

construction of steam engines, and the design of artillery shells. Cayley's work in heavy engineering, especially the design of railway equipment, was well recognized in his own day.

In recent times, considerable evidence has been uncovered revealing the remarkable extent of Cayley's work, which began as far back as the 1790's. Bringing together all the existing knowledge (in 1661 another brilliant Englishman, Robert Hooke, had written an important treatise, *Resistance of Air to Bodyes Moved Through It*), Cayley formulated his basic approach to the problem of flight: "to make a surface support a given weight by the application of power to the resistance of air. . . ." He then proceeded to work out many of the practical problems connected with the creation of a flyable aircraft. Rightly convinced of the correctness of his approach to airplane design, Cayley predicted over a hundred and fifty years ago the movement of "passengers and goods more securely by air than by water, and with a velocity of from twenty to one hundred miles per hour. . . ."

Interestingly, illustrations of the principle of flight had existed long before Cayley's work or even that of Da Vinci. The lifting of a kite in the wind, the force generated by the sails of windships—both were ancient examples of what could be accomplished by the movement of air against a resisting surface. The ordinary kite is a prime example; it is in fact a kind of tethered glider, an unpowered airplane held stationary in a flow of air. The principle is simple: the lifting force is created by the push of the air against the underside of an *inclined surface*—a surface set so that its edge is raised at a slight angle to the airflow. (This angle is termed the "angle of attack.") Obviously, the lifting effect will be the same if the flow is created by the movement of the surface through the air—this, in fact, is the essence of the flight of an airplane.

Cayley realized that this was the answer to the riddle of flight, and, being a practical engineer as well as a theoretician, he then proceeded to the design of aircraft that could actually fly. Of necessity, two questions in particular had to be answered: how to propel the lifting surface (wing) through the air, and then how to stabilize the wing so that it would maintain the correct angle of attack to the air. Eventually the solutions came, but with one important exception—he could not overcome the lack of a suitable engine.

In 1809 Cayley described an experimental internal combustion engine built by a friend, William Chapman, that used benzine as a fuel. The device was impractical—the cost of running it was eight times that of a steam engine of the day. But, in commenting on this failure, Cayley plainly foresaw the modern internal combustion engine. "Probably a much cheaper engine might be produced," he wrote, "by a gas-tight apparatus and by firing the inflammable air generated with a due proportion of common air under a piston."

Although he was stymied by the lack of a suitable engine, this British pioneer's work was nevertheless so remarkable that in his own day he was recognized as the "Father of Aerial Navigation." Of his little-known achievements, perhaps the most remarkable was a monoplane glider with most of the important features of a modern aircraft. There is strong evidence, recently uncovered, that this glider actually flew at Brampton in the 1850's, if not earlier. The details of the incident are based upon the accounts of a long-forgotten eyewitness, Cayley's granddaughter, and his paper, written in 1852, misleadingly titled "Governable Parachutes." Published in the *Mechanic's Magazine* of London that year, the paper went unrecognized for over a century; it described, with drawings, an aerodynamically sound glider with a movable tail surface. From other records, and the granddaughter's account, it would seem that this glider, or another very much like it, with Cayley's coachman as pilot, flew some 500 yards from the top of a hill at his Brampton estate, probably in the year 1852. (Cayley was then almost eighty years old.)

Remembered largely for his fixed-wing experiments, Sir George Cayley pioneered in rotating-wing aircraft design as well, and the drawings for at least one machine of the helicopter type have survived. His earliest aeronautical work, a twin-rotor helicopter model built in 1792 when he was nineteen, resembled the device constructed by Launoy and Bienvenu in 1784. Half a century later, in 1842, he credited this first effort

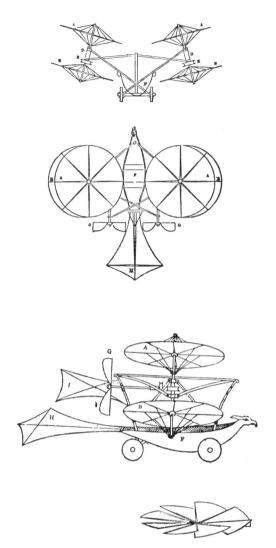

2. *Cayley made these drawings for a vertical take-off and landing aircraft in 1843. Although the design looks fanciful by modern standards, it has features that have appeared in successful helicopters (the wide fanlike rotors resemble those used on the de Bothezat machine flown by the U.S. Army in 1922; the lateral side-by-side arrangement of the rotors is similar to the recordbreaking Focke helicopters built in Germany in the late 1930's). One especially interesting feature is the design of the blades: they flatten down to form a solid disc and act as a wing in forward flight. The bird's-head bowsprit may have been a deliberately humorous touch.*

with the inspiration for his later work. With rotating-wing aircraft, Cayley appears to have accomplished less—at least in terms of models that could fly—than with his fixed-wing designs.

Nevertheless, with vertical-rising helicopter types as well as with fixed-wing, Cayley was uncannily prophetic in describing what would be needed. In a letter sent to the *Mechanic's Magazine* in 1843, he emphasized that the ability to take off straight up, hover, and land in tight areas was important.

"Aerial navigation by mechanical means must depend upon surfaces moving with considerable velocity through the air, but these vehicles will ever be inconvenient, not to say absolutely inefficient . . . for, to be of ordinary use, they must be capable of landing at any place where there is space to receive them, and of ascending again from that point. They should likewise be capable of remaining stationary, or nearly so, in the air, when required."

He added: "Very great power, in proportion to the weight of the engine, is necessary."

In the light of what we now know, Cayley's design for a helicopter seems ponderous, but it faced up to the major problems. The two sets of lifting rotors turned in opposite directions to cancel out torque. Two pusher propellers in the rear were intended to drive the craft through the air, and twin rudders were furnished for steering. An intriguing feature was the ability of the large fanlike rotors (eight blades for each rotor) to close down flat to form a lifting surface for forward flight.

Encouraged by Cayley's work, another Englishman, W. H. Phillips, designed a small steam-powered model helicopter that flew in 1842; it seems to have been the very first model aircraft in history to fly powered by an engine rather than with springs, clockwork, elastic whalebone or other such wind-up contrivances. The little single-rotor model incorporated a form of rotor drive not unlike the tipjet systems used on a few modern helicopters. Steam from a miniature boiler passed up through the hollow rotor shaft and out to rearward-facing holes at the tips of the blades; in effect, a form of jet propulsion. Although a steam system was impractical for a man-carrying aircraft because it was far too heavy, the Phillips model—exhibited at the Crystal Palace in London in 1868—had considerable effect on the scientific thought of the day and encouraged others to strive for more efficient engines.

After Cayley, the deluge. He died in 1857, and during the last half of the nineteenth century there were helicopter inventors everywhere—but no flyable helicopters. The most critical problem of course was still the lack of a suitable engine.

If practical results were not forthcoming, there was one memorable advance achieved during this period by an enthusiastic French pioneer, Viscomte Gustave de Ponton d'Amecourt, who was responsible for the creation of the word "helicopter."* D'Amecourt was instrumental in further rotating-wing research, heading a small band of prophets and enthusiasts who were passionately involved with the dream of the helicopter. Others in the group included Gabriel de la Landelle and the early photographer Félix Nadar. A contemporary description of these three proponents of vertical flight was the "Triumvirat Hélicoidal." D'Amecourt built a small steam-driven model of his design (still in the French Air Museum) in 1863 and took out French and British patents on it. Impressed with the work of the group, Jules Verne later wrote a science-fiction novel, published in 1886, that was titled *Robur le conquerant*. The hero of this epic cruised the skies in a giant helicopter.

Another notable French experimenter of this time was Alphonse Pénaud. Around 1870 he built a number of high-flying model helicopters, all fashioned after the manner of the Chinese top. Powered with twisted rubber bands, several of his models climbed to heights of more than 50 feet. Pénaud's experimentation and model-building activity was not limited to helicopters alone: he designed and constructed tiny rubber-powered airplanes and ornithopters (wingflappers) that also flew exceedingly well.

As the age of steam progressed, other experimenters persevered. In 1878, powered by an ingenious 7.7-pound engine,

---

* A detailed description of the origins of the word "helicopter"—as well as other names that have been used for rotating-wing aircraft—is provided in the Appendix.

a steam-driven model built by an Italian, Enrico Forlanini, flew to a height of 30 feet and remained in the air for all of thirty seconds. Although these tests with steam-engine-propelled models were interesting and often encouraging, they were not meaningful in terms of the construction of a successful man-carrying aircraft. The steam engines of the day were simply too heavy for a full-scale helicopter; they required massive cylinders and valves, a boiler, a fire box—not to mention a sky-high fireman to tend it. If a suitable lightweight engine had been available, the next step would have been the flight of some sort of experimental rig in order to perfect the aircraft, particularly the rotor and its control system. But without an engine this first basic step of trial-and-error testing was impossible. Understandably, the development of the helicopter would await the perfection of the lightweight gasoline engine.

The key, as Cayley had said, would be to build an engine with very great power in proportion to its weight. This is one of the important reasons why the fixed-wing airplane was to be perfected before the helicopter. With the fixed-wing approach it was possible to fly an engineless glider, perhaps first as a kite and then later in free flight; something might then be learned about improving the craft and its control system without troubling about an engine. At the turn of the century the Wright brothers had at first been fascinated with the idea of the helicopter, but lacking a suitable engine they had turned to the concept of the airplane. Their experiments had followed the same sensible pattern as those of Sir George Cayley: the glider was first flown as a kite and then in free flight. Encouraged by these experiments, eventually they built their own engine which was—just barely—of sufficient power. The Wrights, significantly, rated Cayley as the most important of the nineteenth-century experimenters. In 1912 Orville Wright wrote: "Sir George Cayley was a remarkable man. . . . He knew more of the principles of aeronautics than any of his predecessors, and as much as any that followed him up to the end of the nineteenth century."

Another element favoring the early airplane researchers is the fact that a much more powerful engine is needed for a helicopter than for an airplane of equivalent weight; it was easier to fly by sliding along on a wing than by trying to drive an "airscrew" straight up into the air.

In the 1880's the outstanding electrical inventor of the day, Thomas Edison, looked into the problem of helicopter flight. His comments were much to the point: "I got up a motor and put it on the scales and tried a number of different things and contrivances [rotors?] connected to the motor to see how it would lighten itself on the scale. I got some data and made up my mind that what was needed was a very powerful engine for its weight." The motor Edison used in these experiments was electrical. The internal combustion engine that Cayley had recommended was still unperfected, and Edison went back to another old idea, the gunpowder engine, actually a primitive form of the internal-combustion engine. Designed with a gun-cotton tape that was fed into the engine automatically and then exploded by an electric spark, it seemed promising—that is, until it blew up, along with part of Edison's laboratory. Despite this excitement, Edison still favored the helicopter, even after the first airplanes were flying: "Whatever progress the aeroplane might make, the helicopter will come to be taken up by advanced students of aeronautics." His words had the sure ring of prophecy.

At last, after the turn of the century, a new lightweight power plant became available. Fitted to the early automobiles and box-kite airplanes, the gasoline engine began to prove itself. In 1907, four years after the Wright brothers had flown the first controllable airplane, French designer Louis Bréguet built a primitive helicopter that could lift a man into the air.

It was a time of the flowering of arts and sciences in France. Although the first airplane had been flown in the United States, for the first decade the French, with Gallic passion and enthusiasm, led the world in aviation research and progress. The helicopter was a case in point, for the first machines to fly were French. The inspiration stemmed, perhaps, from the "Triumvirat Hélicoidal" of fifty years before.

A purist might scorn the first hops in the year 1907 as not

actually being flights, since the machine was held steady by four assistants to prevent any erratic movement. But the Bréguet-Richet "Gyroplane No. 1" did take a Monsieur Volumard—chosen for his light weight—into the air for the first time on August 24, 1907. The machine rose only to a height of about two feet, remaining in the air for one minute. Unhappily, it was not sufficiently steady or controllable for free flight, and eventually testing was discontinued in favor of building a completely new machine.

The first true flight, free of any tie-down ropes, apparently was made by Paul Cornu, in another French machine later the same year, on November 13. His helicopter had two rotors mounted in tandem, one behind the other. The pilot sat between them, in intimate proximity to the little 24-horsepower Antoinette engine. The helicopter rose no more than 6 feet, and the longest flight lasted only a third of a minute. Nevertheless, it flew, completely free of any attachment to the ground. Today it would be said that the pilot "had not gotten out of ground effect."* To steer, to rock the ship from side to side, or to nose up and down, there were movable flat surfaces—control vanes—mounted under the rotors so the airflow would push against them. The system on the Cornu machine was ineffectual, though control vanes were used with better effect on later aircraft.

The following year Bréguet produced his second helicopter. It was furnished with twin 25-foot rotors, powered by a 55-horsepower Renault engine, with a set of biplane wings for good measure. On July 22, 1908, it rose vertically to the respectable height of 15 feet and flew for a short period of time, apparently under control, but the machine was completely wrecked upon landing.

During the period when these two marginal successes were achieved, there occurred a noteworthy failure. A small twin-rotor type was built in Czarist Russia by student Igor I. Sikor-

---

* When a helicopter is hovering near the surface, a thick layer of air builds up between the rotor and the surface of the ground, owing to interference with the downflow. This ground cushion—ground effect—provides additional lift as long as the helicopter remains near the surface; when it flies up away from the ground cushion, the extra lift is lost and the pilot must apply more power.

3. Not first in free flight but first into the air nevertheless was this tethered test rig, the Bréguet-Richet Gyroplane No. 1, first flown on August 24, 1907. Powered by a 45-horsepower engine, it had four separate rotor units, one at each corner of a cross-shaped frame. Each rotor in turn consisted of four biplane blades, a total of thirty-two lifting surfaces. Anchored so it could only move straight up, the machine was far from a flyable aircraft. But it proved, for the first time, that powered rotors could actually lift the weight of pilot and machine into the air.

4. *Because many early machines were capable of short hops into the air, it is difficult to pinpoint the first that actually flew. Generally accepted as the trail breaker was this fragile twin-rotor aircraft flown by Paul Cornu in France on November 13, 1907. Unlike the tethered helicopter tested by Bréguet earlier the same year, the Cornu machine managed to hover in free flight without any attachment to the ground. The flight lasted only twenty seconds, but it marked the beginning of an era. A 24-horsepower engine drove the paddle-shaped rotors through a belt-drive system.*

5. *Kiev, 1910: with a wrench clasped in one hand, student engineer Igor I. Sikorsky stands proudly next to the wooden frame of a rudimentary coaxial helicopter. Rebuilt from his unsuccessful 1909 design, it still failed to lift, although Sikorsky had cut the weight and redesigned the rotors, increasing the over-all diameter. Undaunted, the young Russian inventor turned to airplanes and used the 25-horsepower Anzani engine from the helicopter to power his first airplane, which flew in June of 1910. Sikorsky prospered with airplanes and emigrated to the United States when the Russian Revolution began.*

sky. The machine could lift its own weight of 400 pounds but not the weight of a pilot. A coaxial design with two sets of rotors turning in opposite directions on the same mast, the machine shook and vibrated heavily during ground tests and was never flown. After a second failure in 1910 Sikorsky abandoned helicopters for airplanes, built the first four-engined aircraft in the world, and eventually went on to found a major aircraft company in the United States. But fortunately for the world of helicopters, he returned to his first love and over thirty years later, perfected his first successful helicopter at his company's plant in Connecticut.

Another significant Russian design dating from this period was the modern-looking single-rotor helicopter built by student Boris N. Yuriev in Moscow in 1912. The machine had a small antitorque rotor at the tail and a two-bladed main rotor, antedating the configuration in wide use today by almost thirty years. Powered by the same 25-horsepower Anzani engine favored by many of the early experimenters, it was an ultralight

6. *The lightweight helicopter designed and built by student Boris N. Yuriev at Moscow in 1912 shows a surprisingly modern configuration: a single two-bladed main rotor with an anti-torque rotor at the tail. During ground testing the main drive shaft broke, and development ceased with the onset of World War I.*

wooden frame aircraft weighing only 445 pounds. Unfortunately, the main drive shaft broke during ground run-up tests and work ceased. Yuriev went on to supervise the development of helicopters at the Soviet Central Aero-Hydrodynamic Institute, beginning in 1925. The patriarch of Russian rotary-wing aviation, he died in 1962.

If two Russian attempts had failed, the two French successes were only marginal; the Bréguet and Cornu machines had flown, but just barely. Although the "flights" of 1907 and 1908 were milestones in the fulfillment of the dream, they could not compare with the development of the airplane in that period. The Wright brothers in their airplane had demonstrated steady flights that were under the complete control of the pilot. The copter pioneers could claim daylight under their landing gear, but little else. Their machines were unstable in hovering flight, and the control systems were inadequate or nonexistent. In another area, the question of what happened if the engine failed, the Wright Flyer again had it over the primitive helicopters. With a dead engine, the box-kite Wright plane could, at least, glide. But the Bréguet and Cornu helicopters had no such ability. If their engines stopped, they fell and that was that. Thus, despite the enthusiasm these first flights fired in youthful inventors like Sikorsky, the helicopter was decades behind the fixed-wing airplane. In terms of control, stability, and reliability, it was not until 1936 and 1937 that helicopters could be compared to the first successful airplanes.

The next major improvements were not forthcoming until after World War I. The pattern by then had been established: helicopters would fly after a fashion, but they were not as yet controllable in flight. The next batch of inventors had their work cut out for them. This was to increase the duration of the time the machine could stay in the air while at the same time trying to perfect control systems that would enable the pilot really to fly.

The war had, of course, stimulated aeronautical development; in an astonishingly short period of time the airplane grew from a crackpot invention into a reasonably effective weapon. Lighter, more powerful engines were perfected, and these became available as cheap surplus in the postwar period. One type of engine in particular, the now-extinct rotary, was a favorite with helicopter and Autogiro experimenters of the early 1920's; though none too reliable, it was light and powerful.

The rotaries were air-cooled engines, designed so that the entire crankcase, cylinders and all—with the propeller attached —could turn freely in bearings and rotate *around* the crankshaft. (This was a startling departure from the standard engine, which had a stationary crankcase and a rotating crankshaft.) The crankshaft of the rotary was fixed firmly to the mount, and the force of the power strokes caused the whole mass, prop and engine together, to spin away merrily, usually on the order of 1,300 revolutions per minute. The idea behind this unorthodox arrangement was to ensure good cooling; with the crankcase rotating at this speed, a strong flow of air was forced over the cylinders.

The main advantage of the World War I rotaries lay in their weight: they were lighter than other types, offering the highest power-to-weight ratio of any engine of that day. This was because they were the only type of air-cooled engine that worked, at a time when the competition consisted mainly of heavy water-cooled engines with radiators, water jackets, pumps, and other accessories. Air-cooled engines need no such extras; the cylinders are furnished with aluminum fins to dissipate heat in the blast of air flowing over the engine. Today, air-cooled piston engines (stationary, not rotary) are used universally in aviation.

The first successful rotary, manufactured in France, was the 50-horsepower Gnôme, which powered the Henry Farman box-kite airplanes of 1909 and 1910. Other French rotaries that followed included the Monosoupape, Clerget, Le Rhône and Gnôme-Rhône. Manufactured in different marks, ranging from 80 to 180 horsepower, the Le Rhône in particular seemed to have been a favorite choice of the helicopter experimenters. During the war, the rotaries powered every class of every military airplane; an outstanding example was that fierce little fighter, the Sopwith *Camel*. Those powered by Clerget engines were called, simply, *"Clerget Camels."*

A prime example of a postwar helicopter powered by a rotary engine was the large four-rotor machine designed for the U.S.

7. *This rare photograph marked 1914 shows the little-known helicopter built by Danish aviation pioneer Jens C. H. Ellehammer with its landing gear clear of the ground. The vague silhouette shows a highly advanced design for its day: coaxial, with two rotors turning in opposite directions to cancel out torque. The short rotor blades were attached to two circular rotating surfaces; the lower surface, covered with fabric, was intended to serve as a parachute. Ellehammer experimented with fixed-wing aircraft as well as helicopters, and his airplane—reported to have flown in 1906—may have been the first in Europe.*

9. *(Bottom, facing page) The professor and the test pilot: Russian émigré Dr. George de Bothezat and Colonel Thurman H. Bane lean, more or less casually, against the airframe of de Bothezat's experimental helicopter at McCook Field, Dayton, Ohio, on December 18, 1922. Colonel Bane, chief of the U.S. Army Air Service Experimental Station at McCook, flew the four-rotor machine during flight tests.*

8. *Powered by three 120-horsepower airplane engines, this captive observation helicopter was the creation of Stefan Petróczy, a lieutenant in the Austrian Army during World War I. At first the machine failed to perform, but young Professor Theodore von Kármán—who later emigrated and became a leading American aerodynamicist—joined the effort, and eventually the aircraft flew to a height of over 150 feet. Supported by two massive wooden propellers turning in opposite directions, the Petróczy-Von Kármán marvel could lift a pilot, an observer, and enough fuel for an hour in the air. During flight the machine was anchored to the ground by outrigger cables. There is no record that it was developed beyond the experimental stage.*

Army Air Corps by Dr. George de Bothezat, an *émigré* Russian professor who sported a black beard and the style and elegant manners of an old-world academician. Beginning work in the United States in 1921, he designed and constructed a four-rotor machine powered by the 180-horsepower Le Rhône. The main structure consisted of a cross-shaped frame over 60 feet wide, with four huge fan-shaped rotors (six blades each) mounted at each corner. Superficially at least, the wide-swept rotor blades strongly resembled the rotors of Sir George Cayley's vertical take-off aircraft that had been envisioned a century before. It flew for the first time at what was then McCook Field (now Wright Field) on December 18, 1922, with Professor de Bothezat at the controls. The first flight lasted roughly a minute and a half as the ship rose 6 feet in the air, then drifted with the wind and landed some 500 feet away. In comparison to a modern helicopter, the rotor blades turned quite slowly, at about 70 revolutions per minute.

Altogether, the de Bothezat helicopter made over a hundred flights, up to heights of 15 or 20 feet. On one memorable occasion it flew with three and then four men clinging to the outriggers, to demonstrate the machine's stability in an unbalanced and overloaded condition. During the trials, which lasted two years, a larger engine of 220 horsepower was installed.

Despite its ungainly appearance and the limited nature of the flights, the de Bothezat machine showed good control characteristics. Each of the enormous fanlike rotors had an individual collective pitch mechanism (the "bite" of each rotor could be controlled), which was linked to the pilot's control. It received favorable comment from Colonel Thurman H. Bane, who had achieved the historic distinction of becoming the U.S. Army's first helicopter pilot by test-flying the machine; he said that "it is my sincere belief that your helicopter is the biggest aeronautical achievement since the first flight of the Wright Brothers."

Another more than casually interested observer was Thomas Edison, who saw in this machine a fulfillment of his earlier prophecies. In a letter written in February, 1923, Edison hailed de Bothezat's work: "You certainly have made a great advance; in fact, as far as I know, the first successful helicopter." But the accolade was premature; the Army finally abandoned de Bothezat's design, commenting unfavorably on the "general mechanical complexity" as well as other unsatisfactory characteristics. The project had cost $200,000, a lot of money for the fledgling Air Corps to spend on a highly unorthodox aircraft. The best performance figures recorded for the "Flying X" included an altitude of about 30 feet, and the lifting of a total weight (aircraft and payload) of 4,400 pounds.

The same period saw further progress in Europe by another French designer, Etienne Oemichen, whose experiments dated from 1920; several flyable, if bizarre, aircraft were produced. A feature of one machine was the balloon anchored to the top of the frame, and brash spectators may have been inclined to ask if Oemichen was sure that he had invented a helicopter. A later design had four main rotors mounted on a cross-shaped frame—an arrangement simliar to de Bothezat's—with two propellers for propulsion, another for directional control, and *five* more variable-pitch props for control in pitch and roll. For good measure, the system included a large flywheel intended to increase stability.

On April 14, 1924, a machine of this type, minus a balloon but powered by a 180-horsepower Rhône rotary, flew 1,181 feet to establish the first helicopter distance record to be officially recognized by the Fédération Aeronautique Internationale. Later, on May 4 of the same year, this aircraft was the winner of a large cash award from the French Air Ministry for the first circular kilometer flown by a helicopter. A maximum height of 50 feet was reached, and a distance of 5,550 feet covered, with an endurance of fourteen minutes. However strange Oemichen's design might seem today, with its multitude of airscrews (at least one for each different control movement), it made well over a thousand flights, demonstrating control about all three axes, and was therefore a significant improvement over earlier machines.

Hard on the heels of Oemichen's success was another major step forward, again in France, still a center of aeronautical research. A little more than a month after the Oemichen machine had won the Air Ministry prize, a new design by a

10. *A four-rotor de Bothezat helicopter in flight at McCook Field on April 17, 1923, with Colonel Bane at the controls. Flights were made with three and then four men clinging to the outriggers to demonstrate control and lifting ability. Considering that 800 pounds of payload was lifted in fairly steady flight with an engine of only 180 horsepower, the accomplishment was significant. Besides the four main rotors, the machine had two propellers for directional control plus two more in the center of the frame to cool the engine and give added lift.*

11. The Pescara coaxial design of 1924 featured two rotors turning in opposite directions on the same shaft; each rotor consisted of a set of four biplane blades, braced with struts and wires in the fashion of the airplanes of the day. The system worked, and Pescara's machine set a world's record for cross-country flight and pioneered with a pitch-change mechanism for the blades—all sixteen of them. The power plant was a 180-horsepower Hispano-Suiza, the same engine used in the famed SE-5 fighter flown by the British in World War I.

Spanish designer, the Marquis Raul Pateras Pescara, achieved a new world's record. His helicopter flew almost ½ mile in four minutes and eleven seconds at a height of 6 feet—in other words, an exhilarating forward speed of roughly 8 miles an hour. The fact that the award was made for the mere accomplishment of moving in forward flight from one point to another—more or less under control—illustrates one of the major problems of that era. Inventors had gotten the machine off the ground. The next effort was to make it go into forward flight at a reasonable speed without oscillating or capsizing.

Pescara had started experimenting in 1919, and this record-making flight was accomplished with his third helicopter. The aircraft had two coaxial rotors on the same mast, in the manner of the eighteenth-century models of Lomonosov and Launoy and Bienvenu. This seemed a straightforward improvement over the swarms of airscrews that had festooned the De Bothezat and Oemichen ships. Yet, true to the tradition of mechanical gimcrackery and complexity, each rotor was a biplane affair composed of eight individual blades—a total of sixteen lifting surfaces whirling madly around one central shaft, driven by a 180-horsepower Hispano-Suiza engine.

Although the machine was not steady in the air, lacking stability, it incorporated many important features found on modern helicopters. For control, the blades could be warped to change their pitch angle (and thus the angle of attack) while in flight, eliminating the need for auxiliary airscrews. This was a major step forward, since control movements could now be accomplished by the main rotor alone. By way of comparison, to get the same effect Oemichen had been forced to position airscrews all over his machine.

Pescara's machine demonstrated another important improvement. Pitch changes could be made, while in flight, in such a way so as to produce a horizontal movement across the ground.* Through the use of this system, the ship could be

* It is not entirely clear if the Pescara machine was the first to utilize this system. However, it seems to have been the very first to actually demonstrate fairly effective control through pitch changes in the main rotors alone. In technical language, the pitch of the blades could be varied both *cyclically* and *collectively*, and this represented a great step forward. (An explanation of these terms is furnished in Chapter VIII.)

made to move in forward flight, foreshadowing the control arrangement used on most modern helicopters.

In the United States, a series of unusual helicopterlike aircraft were built by the father-and-son team of Emile and Henry Berliner in the early 1920's. These machines, powered by Le Rhône rotaries, seemed to be hybrids; a cross between an airplane and a helicopter. Several had side-by-side twin rotors mounted above a set of monoplane, biplane, or even triplane wings. The rotors were rigid wooden airscrews resembling oversize airplane propellers. In several designs control was accomplished by a simple but fairly effective device: sets of movable *vanes*—flat surfaces mounted in strategic positions under the rotors, similar to those used on the Cornu helicopter of 1907. For control, the vanes were moved from a vertical to a horizontal position so that their flat surface was exposed to the blast of air flowing down through the rotors. This force could be used to rock the aircraft from side to side. An advanced version had a small airscrew, connected by a drive shaft to the engine, mounted horizontally at the rear of the fuselage so as to lower or raise the tail.

The Berliners made significant contributions to the state of the art: one of their twin-rotor aircraft made flights of up to 100 yards in length, with a duration in the air of a minute and a half. Yet by the mid-1920's the relatively primitive control arrangement used on aircraft of this type was being overshadowed by the more effective system of pitch control within the main rotor, such as used on the Pescara machine, really a turning point in the development of the helicopter.

Another experiment of the mid-twenties was the helicopter designed by Louis Brennan* at the Royal Aircraft Establishment at England's Farnborough aviation test center. This aircraft was another approach to the problem of eliminating torque, the tendency of the aircraft to twist in the direction opposite to the rotation of the rotor blades. The copter was lifted by one huge 60-foot four-bladed rotor, which, in turn, was driven by small propellers mounted on the tips of two of

* Brennan was known for his work in the development of gyrostabilizer systems, especially for naval torpedoes.

12. *Fascinating "gyrocopters" were the product of father-and-son experiments by Emile and Henry Berliner in the United States between 1909 and 1923. The model shown here combined almost every known flight mechanism into one airframe: three wings resembling the wartime Fokker triplanes, two main rotors that barely cleared the pilot's head, and a tiny tail rotor on top of the fuselage, just forward of the fin, to raise or lower the tail. Other features included vanes mounted in the rotor downwash for lateral control and a mechanical system for inclining the rotor shafts forward. This photograph was taken at historic College Park Airport, near Washington, probably in 1923.*

13. *This magnificently complex Curtiss-Bleecker helicopter of 1930 was an unsuccessful venture by an old established aircraft company, Curtiss-Wright, into the unknown and mysterious world of rotating wings. The machine was a near-heroic attempt to eliminate the problem of torque by providing each massive rotor blade with its own propeller to spin it around the boat-shaped fuselage. Rotor control surfaces projected behind each blade. The propellers were driven through a gear and shaft system from the centrally mounted Pratt and Whitney* Wasp *engine. According to the* Aircraft Year Book *of 1931, "In 1930 . . . it remained an unknown quantity . . . It had been hopped off the ground in the still air of its hangar several times, but engineers in charge of the project were not yet ready for flight tests."*

the four blades. This meant, of course, drive shafts running down the length of the blades connecting through a gear box to a 230-horsepower Bentley BR-2 rotary engine of 1917 vintage. (The same approach was used in the design of the huge, complex Curtiss-Bleecker, which managed a few short hops in the United States in 1930.)

Unwieldy though this drive system was, the Brennan design incorporated—as did the Pescara—the new idea of pitch control for the rotor blades, not by mechanical linkage—as used on the Pescara—but through small aerodynamic surfaces for warping the blades, resembling the control tabs found on airplanes. This British helicopter flew some seventy or eighty short flights close to the ground before a final crash in October, 1925. The performance of the machine was typical of many of the experimental helicopters of the 1920's: fairly docile in hovering flight but difficult to handle when in forward flight.

This approach, a single torqueless rotor driven by some kind of a push or pull at the tips of the rotors, is still with us. A number of small copters have been built since World War II that use this principle, but with jets instead of propellers on the blade tips to drive the rotors. Between 1929 and 1935, a determined Italian inventor, Vittorio Isacco, working in various countries as he searched for financial support, produced several aircraft of a type similar to the Brennan helicopter. Isacco's design—which he termed a "Helicogyre"—used the same arrangement, propellers mounted on the tips to turn the rotor, but he eliminated the long drive shafts in the rotor blades. His approach was to place small engines at the blade tips to turn the driving propellers. His first two machines, which did not fly, were built in France. Both were powered by twin Anzani engines, driving 6-foot propellers mounted at the tips of a two-bladed rotor that was 40 feet in diameter. Isacco moved to Britain, where he built his third model in 1930. This remarkable aircraft had three engines, two small Armstrong-Siddeley *Cherub* engines, one on each rotor blade, and a larger Genet in the nose, airplane fashion, to help propel the ship in forward flight; today we might call this kind of cross between airplane and helicopter propulsion a "compound" helicopter.

Undaunted by the failure of this design, too, Isacco next took up residence in Soviet Russia and built between 1932 and 1935, a still larger and more complex helicogyre. This fourth aircraft had a four-bladed rotor and, needless to say, was intended as a five-engined aircraft. Development ceased when the inventor had to leave the country with the beginning of Stalin's purges and the expulsion of foreign engineers and technicians.

No review of the helicopter in this period would be complete without a description of a design by a Dutch inventor, A. G. von Baumhauer, which he developed between 1924 and 1930. The Hollander built a straightforward machine reminiscent of the Yuriev aircraft of 1912. It had one main rotor and one small airscrew at the tail, pointing sideways, to counteract the torque effect. With all needed control functions accomplished either by manipulating the main rotor blades or the tail rotor, von Baumhauer's ship strongly resembled the configuration used for many helicopters today. The aircraft was not particularly successful, however; it had that useless mechanical complexity found on most early helicopters, even the better ones. Rather than use a drive shaft to drive the pinfeather rotor at the rear, a whole extra engine was positioned in the tail. The added complication and weight tended to cancel out the advantages of the small tail rotor for torque control. The copter made many hovering flights but never rose more than a few feet off the ground.

Still another promising design during this period was produced by Oscar von Asboth in Hungary. His fourth helicopter, the AH-4, used two rotors in a coaxial system powered by a tiny 110-horsepower Clerget rotary engine of World War I ancestry. By midsummer of 1930 it was reported to have climbed to a height of 100 feet and covered almost 2 miles at about 12 miles per hour. Like its contemporaries, it could fly out of ground effect, and it was fairly stable in hovering flight, but it had only marginal control and could not manage any speed in forward flight.

An Italian helicopter designed by Corradino d'Ascanio and flown by Marinello Nelli in October of 1930 established a new world record for altitude, time in the air, and cross-country distance flown. It rose to a height of 59 feet, remained aloft for eight minutes and forty-five seconds, and slowly flew a distance of 3,538.7 feet. These statistics serve to illustrate what was considered record-breaking performance for a helicopter in 1930. The machine was a coaxial type, with two 43-foot rotors powered by a 95-horsepower Fiat engine. The control system included a form of pitch control in the main rotors, plus three variable-pitch propellers positioned in key positions around the airframe, thus combining two different methods. As with the other helicopters of the day, stability and control were marginal.

In the Soviet Union, starting in 1931, Yuriev's Central Aero-Hydrodynamic Institute (TsAGI) began to produce a series of single-rotor helicopters of considerable refinement. These machines had two small antitorque rotors, one mounted forward of the nose, the other at the tail. First in the series was the 1-EA, reported as having noteworthy performance, including one remarkable climb to 2,000 feet, before being wrecked in an accident. A newer version, the 3-EA, flew in 1933, achieving a maximum forward speed of 13 miles per hour and flights of ten to fifteen minutes' duration. Another in the series, the 5-EA, flew successfully in 1934, exhibiting characteristics similar to the earlier models and a high degree of stability.

During the early 1930's inventors and researchers began to sense that total success had to be close at hand. Helicopters had flown well out of ground effect, to considerable altitude. Stability and control were improving. Still lacking, however, was the ability to fly at a reasonable forward speed. Another important shortcoming was the need for some means of being able to glide or otherwise descend safely in case of engine failure. Besides this, there was the general unreliability to be expected of newly designed mechanisms; years of testing would be required before they could be trusted. In the early 1930's helicopter development had reached a stage comparable to that of the Wright airplane thirty years before. Like the early airplane the helicopter had proved that it could barely fly, but not much else.

Yet the situation was about to change radically. From a

14. A helicopter with a modern-looking main rotor was developed by the Dutch designer Dr. A. G. von Baumhauer between 1924 and 1930. It had an anti-torque tail rotor, similar to the configuration perfected by Sikorsky a decade later. Unhappily, Von Baumhauer chose to drive the rear rotor with an entire extra engine mounted in the tail, a heavy and unwieldy complication. The aircraft achieved brief hovering flights and was reported to have crashed.

separate line of development (independent of the helicopter), had come a successful rotorcraft, the Autogiro, whose principle of flight was entirely different from the helicopter: the aircraft flew with a free-spinning rotor that was not powered by its engine. Elements of the Autogiro would be adapted, leading to the creation of a truly practical helicopter.

There were other forces at work that would accelerate the process. In Germany a murderous regime was planning world conquest and creating a new war machine. As the world struggled to rearm, enormous sums would be spent on new warplanes and funds would eventually flow down to the men struggling with the vision of straight-up flight. The stage was set.

II

A Spanish Windmill

"Autorotation is a fundamentally different phenomenon from windmilling. The rotor blades of the Autogiro are actually flying into the wind, exactly as an airplane flies forward. . . ."
—JUAN DE LA CIERVA, inventor of the Autogiro
"To land in a vertical descent! Think of it! And not roll a foot forward. . . ."
—CAPTAIN FRANK M. HAWKS, after flying an Autogiro

A HALF-FORGOTTEN PHASE in the history of aviation is the story of the unique, even mysterious, Autogiro.* Invented in 1923, the Autogiro was a rotating-wing aircraft which resembled the helicopters that would first appear ten or fifteen years later, but its flight was based upon an entirely different principle. Unlike the powered rotor of the helicopter, the blades of the Autogiro are freewheeling and not connected in any way to its engine. Their turning depends entirely upon *autorotation,* a phenomenon resulting from the flow caused by the flight of the aircraft through the air. And, significantly, the blades turn *into and against* the flow from the front, at a positive angle, not *with* the airflow as do the vanes of a windmill.

Most rotorplanes, those of the 1920's and the 1930's and the

* The word "Autogiro" was coined by the inventor, Juan de la Cierva, as a proprietary name. When spelled with a small "a," however, it can and frequently has been used as a generic term for this type of aircraft; other generic terms include "autogyro," "rotorplane," or simply "giro." The word "Gyroplane" has also been used for certain specific aircraft.

few recent designs as well, have long, slender rotor blades mounted on a mast above a fuselage much like that of an airplane. An engine and propeller are at the front, and more or less standard control surfaces are positioned at the tail (on early models, small stub wings also projected from the fuselage).

The mast above the fuselage is tilted back at a slight angle with the effect that, as the aircraft is pulled through the air by its propeller, the "relative airflow" is always from the front and below—the condition necessary for autorotation. As long as the aircraft keeps moving forward through the air, the rotor keeps turning. If the engine is slowed down, or even stopped, the Autogiro is balanced so that it will go into a steep but slow descent; the airflow is still coming up from the front and below, and the rotor blades will continue to autorotate.

Oddly, the principle of autorotation seems to have been known long before the first Autogiro took to the air. It is thought that, as early as the Middle Ages, the masters of windmills understood they could get the wind wheels to turn into the airflow, rather than with it, by setting the sails at a very flat angle to the wind. Another example, further removed from the dream of rotating wings, is the ability to tack a sailing ship well up into the eye of the wind and still have the ship move forward; the wind can actually be striking the sail from an angle to the front, and yet the ship will be moving at an angle more or less *against* the force of the wind. And still another model is to be found in nature itself, in the whirling flight of the maple-leaf seedlet, which has the form of a beautifully shaped single-blade rotor.

Whatever the cause, it is obvious that some of the earliest of the twentieth-century experimenters were aware of the possibilities of autorotation as a way of making a power-off descent with a rotorcraft. In 1912, more than ten years before the flight of the first Autogiro and more than twenty before the first successful helicopters, the young experimenter Boris N. Yuriev noted the work of a fellow Russian, a student, dealing with autorotation. During his experiments the student, Sorokovmovskii, had shown that the blades of a large rotor

AUTOROTATION

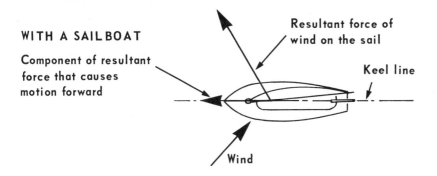

WITH A SAILBOAT

Component of resultant force that causes motion forward

Resultant force of wind on the sail

Keel line

Wind

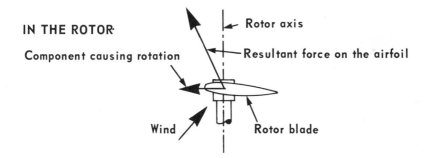

IN THE ROTOR

Component causing rotation

Rotor axis

Resultant force on the airfoil

Wind

Rotor blade

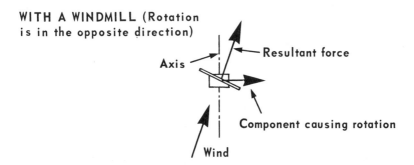

WITH A WINDMILL (Rotation is in the opposite direction)

Axis

Resultant force

Component causing rotation

Wind

15. As this illustration shows, the curved airfoil shape of the blade shifts the resultant force obtained from the airflow (wind) so that the rotor turns in the same direction as if it were under power.

would keep turning of their own volition during a descent and this could be used to make a safe landing, and even to glide forward. Yuriev called this rotor gliding and it appears that he realized it might be used as a means of landing a helicopter safely in the event of an engine failure.

While the principle of autorotation was certainly known, it was thought of primarily as a desirable feature to incorporate in the helicopter, when and if it was invented, not as the basis for an entirely new kind of flying machine. And the Autogiro really was something new under the aeronautical sun. Both the airplane and the helicopter had been dreamed of and tinkered with for years, but no one was quite prepared for this hybrid that seemed to be a cross between the newly invented airplane and the not-quite-invented helicopter.

It is almost too poetic to think that the Autogiro was invented in the land where the great writer and dramatist Cervantes created his comic knight Don Quixote to charge at windmills, but it is nevertheless a sober fact. On January 9, 1923, a young Spanish engineer of aristocratic family and finances named Juan de la Cierva y Cordonia* watched the flight of his first successful Autogiro at Getafe Airdrome near Madrid. His fourth experimental design, this tiny machine had been built up on the fuselage of an old Hanriot scout biplane used by the Allies in World War I.

Cierva's Autogiro was powered by a Le Rhône rotary engine, also of World War I vintage. Above the fuselage, a four-bladed rotor turned smoothly on the mast mounted just over the pilot's open cockpit. For good measure, small winglike ailerons projected on each side of the fabric-covered fuselage, a feature that was to remain with the Autogiro for the next decade. The test pilot was an Army lieutenant, Alejandro Gomez Spencer, in Cierva's words "a Spanish gentleman whose surname and appearance both indicate an English ancestry," and "when we came to the final test the machine lifted at last from the ground, flew steadily across the field and landed

---

* Spanish tradition calls for the use of two surnames; that of the mother's family as well as the father's: "Cierva" indicates the father's name and "Cordonia" the mother's. Hereafter in the text only "Cierva" will be used.

16. *The historic Autogiro in these photographs made its first flight, a short straight-ahead hop, at Getafe Airdrome on January 9, 1923. According to the inventor, the secret of success lay in the rotor blades that were "free to move in a sort of flapping motion wherever they liked according to the effects of the air upon them."*

safely." While it does not sound very impressive, every would-be helicopter designer of that day was struggling desperately to achieve no more than this.

The origins of Cierva's inspiration, a brilliant approach that was independent of the contemporary work in helicopters, are not entirely clear. He had been a designer of fixed-wing aircraft, and his most impressive airplane, a three-engined bomber built for the Spanish Army, had crashed in 1919. Apparently the large biplane had been lost while flying at low speed close to the ground. As Cierva reported, the pilot "had become over-confident, misjudged by a little his minimum flying speed and got himself into trouble too close to the ground . . ." The designer underscored his appraisal of the accident by saying: "Had the same thing happened while he was flying high, he could probably have recovered control and brought the ship safely down"—in other words, the same hazard that is still with us today: the airplane had been flown "too low and too slow."

Since an airplane depends on its speed through the air for the pressure on its wings necessary to support it, slowing up too much will mean the wings will stop lifting; this is what an airplane pilot calls a "stall." You can then dive to pick up speed—if you are high enough. But the pilot of the new trimotor had been too close to the ground. The result was a mass of tangled wreckage from which the pilot, a Captain Rios, managed to emerge safe except for a few superficial cuts and bruises. Brooding about the crash of the trimotor, which he felt might have ended his career as an aircraft designer, the inventor turned to the problem of building an aircraft that could fly slowly and would be stall-proof.

It is not certain just how Cierva seized upon the principle of autorotation in order to create a new kind of aircraft as a solution to the problem. His writings indicate that he was searching for a way to give the wing "a motion of its own, independently of the forward motion of the whole machine." This of course suggests the helicopter, but he sidestepped the idea of a powered rotor and all the mechanical complexity (which he detested) that went with it. Experience had shown, he said, that rotating wings could be put into motion without any application of power. From this appreciation of autorotation he proceeded to the idea of mounting the rotating wings on a shaft above a fuselage that was much like an ordinary airplane—engine and propeller, tail assembly, even small wings. Four years of constant experimentation and analysis occupied Cierva between the crash of his bomber and the flight of his first successful rotor plane at the Madrid airfield. A number of flying test beds were built, using parts of World War I airplanes such as the Hanriot scout, in order to try out various rotors, blade settings, and configurations.

There was one key innovation that can be described, without going too deeply into the technical details of Cierva's work. This was the simple, sure solution to the difficulties he experienced in 1921 and 1922 with his first three giros—the ones that couldn't fly. These early machines had served to demonstrate that the blades would rotate and produce a lifting force as the aircraft ran along the ground, building up speed for the take-off. But when about to become airborne, the rotorplanes showed an alarming tendency—they started to lift up on one wheel and began to roll over.

Searching for a clue to explain this unhappy characteristic, Cierva discovered that the rolling effect was due to the unequal lift forces produced by the blades at different points as they moved around their circular path. His own explanation at the time was that the blades, as they advanced on one side against the onrushing airflow from the front, created more lift on one side than on the other, where they were turning away from the airflow; "the blades on one side of the craft would be going forward while those on the other were going backward, so that there would be much more lift on one side of the machine than the other." The somewhat ungrammatical term often used to describe this phenomenon, "dissymetry of lift," is one of the key phrases in rotating-wing jargon.

In the course of his experiments, Cierva perfected a simple means for overcoming the capsizing effect. A number of tiny rubber-band-powered models had been built to test his theories, and one among many, oddly, flew quite well. This model had been designed with long flexible blades made of rattan, and eventually Cierva realized that this was the reason for its success. The flexibility, he reasoned, permitted each blade to flap up and down as it turned, constantly changing its angle of attack and thus adjusting the lift force; the upward-flapping blade lost some of its bite and spilled lift while the downward-flapping blade gained lift. This feature was incorporated in his next Autogiro, designed with blades that were as flexible as possible, with a hinge at the hub so each blade could flap up and down. Pure trial-and-error research, but it worked. The reasons accepted today as to why the hinged rotor, later used in helicopters, was so successful are complex; an elementary description is provided in Chapter IX. It is interesting to note that the flapping-hinge concept was not new, having been expounded by a French experimenter, Charles Renard, in 1904; it is not clear if Cierva was aware of this. In any case, he was the first to incorporate it in a successful aircraft.

As the Cierva Autogiros appeared, any number of imaginative names were dreamed up, some of them fairly descriptive: "devil's darning needle," "corkscrew plane," "dragonfly," even "a flapper flying machine"; one article that appeared in an American newspaper really went all the way and called it an "autogyroscope." But the name that really caught on, and of course was dead wrong, was "windmill plane." Dr. Cierva may have accepted the windmill for inspirational purposes, but he made short shift of it in his book *Wings of Tomorrow* (1931), while providing a valuable explanation of autorotation that still holds true for the helicopter today:

> But the windmill comparison is incorrect in an important re-
> spect. A windmill's blades are blown around; they do not fly
> around. The direction of the windmill is determined by the angle
> of the under side of the blade, that is, the wind strikes against its
> surface and pushes it around. And the Autogiro's blades actually
> turn in the opposite direction, since the blades have a small positive
> incidence.
>
> Autorotation is a fundamentally different phenomenon from
> windmilling. The rotor blades of the Autogiro are actually flying
> into the wind, exactly as an airplane flies forward at all times and
> can do nothing else. It is an accurate explanation, indeed, to say

17. *Juan de la Cierva, Spanish inventor of the Autogiro, stands with his hand on the propeller of one of his stub-wing rotorplanes: a C-19 Mark III, one of a series of this model built by the A. V. Roe Company in Britain. A machine of this type made the first demonstration flights in public in the United States at the Cleveland air races in August, 1929, and created widespread interest. The two-place open cockpit aircraft was powered by a 100-horsepower Armstrong-Siddeley Genet engine; it cruised at 75 miles per hour and had a top speed of 90.*

that the four blades of the Autogiro are like four airplanes constantly flying or gliding around a central axis. In technical terms it may be stated thus: that the resultant of the blades' lift and its drag is always forward of the vertical axis. In crude paraphase of this it may be said that as it goes against the wind the blade is always travelling downhill, or slightly away from the perpendicular axis of the whole machine. It makes no difference at what angle the Autogiro is climbing or flying. The blades are always gliding toward a point a little below the focus of forward flight. It is impossible, therefore, for autorotation to stop while the machine is going anywhere.

This last point, that it was impossible for the Autogiro's blades to stop turning as long as the ship was moving, raises the question of what happened if the aircraft was slowed up in flight due to engine failure or to the handling of an unskillful pilot. Far from being catastrophic, such a loss in forward speed would serve to demonstrate one of the chief safety features. The machine was balanced so that if the speed dropped below the necessary minumum of 15 or 20 miles per hour, it would simply go into a leisurely descent, almost straight down, and the airflow coming up from below through the rotor would keep it spinning. This, of course, is exactly the same as the autorotational glide of today's helicopters, except that the Autogiro pilot didn't have to perform any special manipulations to set his blades to the right angle—his rotor was *always* in autorotation.

After his initial success in 1923, Cierva continued to develop and perfect the design and then went abroad on demonstration tours. On October 20, 1925, he flew his machine in Britain at the Royal Aircraft Establishment near Farnborough before bemused officials of the British Air Ministry. It was a small aircraft with stub wings, built up on the fuselage of an Avro 504K, the standard British training biplane of World War I, powered with the 100-horsepower Le Rhône rotary engine that had been installed in the Avro. The rotor had four blades constructed, as was the rest of the ship, of wood covered with doped fabric. This particular demonstration was not an unqualified success; Cierva could take off only when there was a moderate wind blowing and there were many attempts when he failed to get the ship airborne. Another evidence of the machine's primitive nature was the means for starting the rotor—a rope was wound about the shaft and a number of men had to run along with it to get the rotor turning up to speed, as a child might spin a top. Nevertheless, there were a few good flights. Those present were certainly impressed; they had never seen any flying machine like it before. For what was essentially a makeshift airframe, it performed well enough to convince the skeptics and the Air Ministry promptly came through with an order for an Autogiro of its own, built in Britain in 1926, again using an Avro 504K fuselage and tail assembly.

This same year, encouraged by British aviation industrialist James G. Weir, Cierva secured financing in England and formed the Cierva Autogiro Company, Ltd. Thereafter, Britain became the center of his activity. Cierva-trained pilots toured Europe, demonstrating the windmill plane while earnestly trying to convince people that the aircraft had nothing to do with windmills. In July, 1926, a Cierva Autogiro was demonstrated for the French Army at the Villacoublay airdrome—the first flight in France. On September fifth of the same year; pilot Frank T. Courtney flew a Cierva machine for the first time in Germany at Tempelhof in Berlin. Courtney would often demonstrate the vertical-descent ability of the giro by climbing to a thousand feet. Then, with the aircraft pointing into the wind, he would bring it almost straight down over a selected point at the airport.

Two years later, on September 18, 1928, Cierva personally flew an Autogiro across the English Channel from Croydon to Le Bourget Airfield near Paris. He followed this up with what must have been one of the most exciting aerial jaunts in history: 3,000 miles across the face of Europe, short leisurely hops in a new type of flying machine that drew crowds everywhere it went.

The effect of this and other successes was to stimulate an intense interest in the Autogiro throughout the world. Further experience proved that the machine could compete—with advantages—against many of the slow airplanes of that day.

18. These two stub-wing Cierva Autogiros were manufactured in England for the British Air Ministry. The aircraft in flight is a C-8, built in 1926, which used the fuselage and other components of an Avro 504K trainer of World War I vintage. Powered by a Le Rhône rotary engine of 110 horsepower, the C-8 had a four-bladed rotor that spanned 39 feet 8 inches; the wide-chord tapered blades are typical of early Cierva machines. The Autogiro on the ground is quite similar but has an in-line water-cooled engine and a larger vertical fin. Both aircraft have ailerons mounted on stub wings for lateral control.

The next decade might easily have been called the golden age of the Autogiro. In all, some five hundred aircraft were built in various parts of the world: in Britain the A. V. Roe, de Havilland, Weir, and Westland companies produced them; in the United States it was Pitcairn (the Autogiro Company of America), and Kellett; in Germany, Focke-Wulf; in France, the Loire Company. And in Russia as well at the TsAGI institute, particularly by N. I. Kamov. Meanwhile, Cierva continued to refine and improve his basic configuration.

After one of the few crashes actually caused by failure of a rotor in flight occurred in February, 1927, he made another important improvement to the rotor head. This consisted of another hinge at the point where each blade attached to the hub. This new hinge was vertical, and it served to allow the blade to pivot slightly forward or to the rear in the plane of rotation. Called a "drag hinge," the name is fairly descriptive— each blade is allowed to drag back a little as it turns. Permitting each blade to move thus helped to relieve the massive stress on the blade root where it attached to the hub. This was another step in the development of the *fully articulated hub,* a rotor head which permits each blade to have as much freedom as possible. The blades are allowed to flap up and down and pivot fore and aft as they turn, hunting for a position where the forces acting on them will be balanced. True to the historical pattern, this refinement eventually became part of the rotor system used on many helicopters today.

One of the particular advantages of the articulated rotor, Cierva felt, was that it did away with the problem of the whirling blades behaving like a giant gyroscope; this factor had been present in the first unsuccessful machines that he had built with rigid rotors. Writing of this, he said:

> It is sufficient to say that it is completely eliminated by the articulation of the rotor blades, which no longer set up a powerful inherent force which must be overcome in order to control the craft. The Autogiro responds as readily to the controls as the most manoeuvrable airplane. If gyroscopic effect were produced by the revolution of the rotor it would be practically impossible to bank the craft for a turn or to bring its nose down or up for a landing.

19. *The first Autogiro to fly in the United States was this Pitcairn-Cierva shown in flight over Bryn Athyn, Pennsylvania. The aircraft was brought over in 1928 for Harold F. Pitcairn, manufacturer of mail planes, and marked the beginning of the association between Cierva and Pitcairn for production of rotorplanes in this country. Classic features of the first-generation Autogiro are evident: stub wings and ailerons, tapered rotor blades, interconnecting cables between the blades. The aircraft, like the earlier C-8, used the fuselage of an Avro 504K biplane. Looking up from the front cockpit is pilot C. J. Faulkner.*

20. *Two stub-wing Autogiros fly over the partially completed George Washington Bridge at New York in September of 1930. The machine in the foreground is the fairly large and powerful PCA-2, powered by a 300-horsepower Wright R-975 engine; it could accommodate two passengers in the front seat. This is the type Amelia Earhart flew when setting her altitude record in 1931; its rate of climb was 1,000 feet a minute and top speed was 123 miles an hour. Many were sold for charter work and for towing advertising banners. The PCA-2 retained the stub wings and ailerons, but it had an auxiliary drive from engine to rotor to start the blades turning.*

Another important innovation was the development of a mechanical starter to bring the rotor up to the necessary speed. The giros of the day needed to have the rotor turning at approximately 100 revolutions per minute before they could take off. With the earlier machines this had been accomplished by starting the rotor with a push by hand and then taxiing the ship on the ground to increase its speed. This need for plenty of space for a take-off run of course handicapped the early Autogiros, though they could still land in a very small area. Later, on his C-19 Mark III giros, manufactured in Britain by A. V. Roe, Cierva incorporated an ingenious device for pre-starting the rotor: the entire horizontal tail surface could be tilted up at an extreme angle so the slipstream from the propeller would be deflected into the rotor. With this arrangement, the airflow from the prop would serve to start the rotor turning. The system worked, but the mechanical starter (which used the direct power of the engine) was still better and was, in fact, the first step in the direction of a powered rotor for the Autogiro.

Refinements of this sort, obviously, were instrumental in improving the performance and reliability of the aircraft. And as this happened, the military services of the major powers became more interested in its possibilities. One of the most interesting and little-known episodes in aviation history were the tests made by the U.S. Army and Navy in the early thirties of Autogiros built by the two leading American manufacturers, Pitcairn and Kellett. The Army was primarily interested in a better vehicle for observation and the spotting of artillery fire, while the Navy was thinking in terms of operations from aboard ship for submarine detection and defense of convoys.

The Navy seems to have been the first to put the rotorplane to the test. In 1931 it contracted with Pitcairn for three of the first series of Autogiros produced by his new plant at Willow Grove, Pennsylvania. Designated the XOP-1 ("X" for experimental, "O" for observation, "P" for Pitcairn), the machines were tested by being assigned to three different roles. One ship flew to Anacostia Field near Washington for trials, later went to sea for tests aboard the aircraft carrier U.S.S. *Langley*.

Another was converted to a seaplane version by installation of floats in place of the standard landing gear. But the third was destined for a very special niche in aviation history.

In the spring of 1932, the third XOP-1 was shipped to a Marine force in Nicaragua where the United States was even then fighting a small undeclared war against insurgents led by the guerrilla chief, Sandino. Shipment of this new and untried aircraft to the scene of jungle warfare seemed a premature move, but the conditions there placed a special premium on the abilities of the Autogiro. The fighting called for close-in support flying from short, primitive airstrips—the dropping of supplies and ammunition, the evacuation of wounded, and the bombing and strafing of pinpoint targets.

Considering the nature of the fighting, assignment of the slow-flying Autogiro, capable of operating from small unprepared landing fields, seemed a reasonable move. But those in command may have looked upon the strange bird with something less than enthusiasm; tests were ordered, but not combat trials under the fire of an enemy. Instead, a board of review was set up to test the XOP-1 against the Marine workhorse biplane, the Vought 02U-1. The tests might very well have been carried out back in the states, but perhaps it was felt that pilots who had actually flown recent combat missions would be the best judge of what the Autogiro could do.

The results of the tests were fairly dismal for the XOP-1. In all fairness, it must be said that the Pitcairn Autogiro was powered by a Wright engine of 300 hundred horsepower, while the 02U-1 strut-and-wire biplane had a 425-horsepower Pratt and Whitney. In the weight-lifting tests, with both crew members and all gear aboard, the XOP-1 could safely handle only fifty pounds of payload. In this condition it could take off with a forward roll of roughly 200 feet and could climb to 1,000 feet in about two minutes. This was inferior to the trusty 02U-1; its broad, wide wings could lift an extra 200 pounds (the weight of a wounded Marine and a stretcher) plus the weight of its crew in about the same take-off distance, with a better rate of climb.

Another failing of the stub-winged XOP-1 was its slow cruising speed and limited range, an important factor for the relatively long-range missions that were the rule in Nicaragua. Marine pilots found that the fully loaded Autogiro cruised at only 70 miles per hour. With its standard three-hour supply of fuel this meant a range of only 210 miles.

There was one bright spot. In one test the slow-flying giro completely outclassed its fixed-wing opponent: the XOP-1 consistently landed on a dime, always hitting the point selected for touchdown with a very short landing run. After the wheels were on the ground, the forward roll was rarely more than 50 feet. Often, when landing into the wind, there was no roll at all; the machine just touched down and stopped. The Autogiro really could come down "like a dandelion seed," as one magazine described it.

An interesting sidelight to the Nicaraguan tests was the enthusiastic reception from the citizens of the capital city of Managua. The Autogiro was a Spanish invention, and as Latin-American people they showed special interest in it. Whatever the feeling may have been about the United States occupation, when the first flight was made at Zacharias Field on June 28, 1932, the local newspapers commented favorably, and crowds of sightseers appeared at the airport to watch the giro go through its paces. As a military aircraft the XOP-1 may have failed, but it did succeed in generating good will for Uncle Sam.

The XOP-1 tests, obviously, were not encouraging. Justifiably, the Navy felt that the Autogiro was seriously lacking, especially in range and load-carrying ability. Eventually, newer types were tested—but the Department's opinion still remained the same: an interesting experiment that might eventually pay off, but the existing models offered too little. If the Navy had persisted, could the giro have played a useful role in the war? The answer remains unclear to this day; but in 1942, when Nazi U-boats were making mincemeat of American ships within sight of our own coasts, then-Senator Harry S. Truman led a congressional committee which criticized the Navy for its failure to develop rotating-wing aircraft.

However, one of the major powers did use rotorplanes as antisubmarine weapons during the war. Beginning in May,

21. *When the performance of the Navy's XOP-1 Autogiro was tested against the Vought 02U-1 biplane in 1932, by Marines in Nicaragua, the XOP-1 came out second best. Here it is shown with the engine cowling off during ground run-up; at the right is the competing 02U-1. The Navy acquired three of the Pitcairn Autogiros in 1931.*

1941, and continuing through the war, the Kayaba Industrial Company in Sendai turned out two hundred and forty Ka-1 giros for the Japanese Army. According to their records, the Ka-1 combined the best features of the American Kellett and the British Cierva aircraft. Intended at first for reconnaissance and the spotting of artillery fire, a number of Ka-1's were modified later in the war to carry 132-pound depth charges for attacks on American submarines. There is no record of a Ka-1 actually sinking a sub, but they may well have participated in attacks on submarines operating near the mainland.

Another employment of the Autogiro in World War II was the missions of a unit in the British Royal Air Force, No. 1448 "Rota" Calibration Flight, equipped with Cierva C-30's. These Autogiros were used in the calibration of the vital radar stations which helped the RAF to beat off the raids of the *Luftwaffe*. A particularly slow-flying aircraft was needed for these missions, one that could remain almost stationary over one spot on the ground. In fact, at the beginning of the war the prevalent method had been the use of captive balloons, but they proved too unwieldy and inefficient. Eventually the unit became No. 529 Autogiro Squadron, based at Henley-on-Thames. During the war it flew almost all the radar calibration missions in Britain, logging over 9,000 hours in the air.

Considering the extent of rotorplane activity in England in the 1920's and the 1930's, it is not surprising that more work went forward there, even during the war years. One project was the development of the Rotachute, a one-man ultra-light rotating wing glider, to be launched from an airplane in flight, for landing agents in occupied Europe. Although they were never used in actual operations, the tiny giros were successful and over twenty were built by the end of the war. Several were sent to the United States, and after the war tiny rotor gliders of this type became available in this country in kit form for aeronautical hobbyists. The Rotachute program led to a larger and even more remarkable glider, consisting of a framework, mast, and rotor that could be easily attached to a small truck. The idea was to perfect a means for actually towing a ground vehicle through the air behind an airplane in the same manner as a fixed-wing glider. This "Rotabuggy" was flown, towed by an airplane, during a number of tests flights over a runway at the Aeroplane Forces Experimental Establishment, Sherburn-in-Elmet, during the latter part of the war. With the coming of peace, development of both the Rotachute and the Rotabuggy ceased. However, it is interesting that a somewhat similar rotor glider—the Fa-330—was also produced in Germany during the war, intended to be towed aloft from the deck of a surfaced submarine as an observation platform.

Turning back to the U.S. Army, the Air Corps apparently began trials with Autogiros a few years after the Navy, experimenting with both Kellett and Pitcairn machines. In 1936 the first two Army giro pilots, Lieutenant (today a retired general) H. F. Gregory and Lieutenant E. S. Nichols were trained at Langley Field, Virginia. The aircraft were Kelletts, a YG-1 and a YG-2. Both were open-cockpit machines that strongly resembled the Pitcairns tested by the Navy in 1932, except that now there were no wings on the fuselage. In this newer direct-control type, the stub wings found on earlier machines such as the Navy's XOP-1 had been dispensed with entirely. The rotor system furnished the lifting force and the means for controlling the ship as well.

The various types of Army Autogiros remained more or less experimental right up to the beginning of World War II. All the standard missions for liaison aircraft were tried with the giros; reconnaissance, spotting of artillery fire, message carrying, and wire laying. By virtue of its very slow flying speed, the Autogiro seemed particularly promising for observing artillery fire. Despite the inevitable problems arising from the use of a new and not entirely perfected aircraft, rotorplane pilots helped lay the groundwork for the work of Army light planes and helicopters in World War II and the Korean War.

Eventually the Air Corps found the appeal of the Autogiro fading. Experience had shown results much the same as those obtained by their tests of the older type in Nicaragua in 1932. The rotorplane could perform well in only a few areas; in most ways it was outclassed by more reliable slow-flying airplanes. There were serious deficiencies, including limited center-of-gravity travel—which meant that any weight put in the wrong place might dangerously affect control of the aircraft—as well as vibrational problems such as control-stick "shake." There was also an especially distressing condition, not fully understood then, called "ground resonance," which could lead the machine to shake itself to pieces while it was still on the ground. And there were unpleasant incidents in flight. During a test of one ship in the late thirties, vibration caused a blade to come off in flight, and the rotating shaft itself broke. The fuselage dove straight in from over 3,000 feet. Fortunately, it was an open-cockpit aircraft, and both the pilot and observer were wearing parachutes. With the rotor gone it was possible to make a clean jump, and the men managed to kick free of the plummeting fuselage. Both parachutes opened, and the men landed unharmed.

But it would be wrong to emphasize too strongly the experience of the military. In the 1930's civilians were doing the work of developing the machine, and the services simply tried out whatever was available, using off-the-shelf aircraft. In the period between the two wars aviation progress depended for the most part on the efforts of small, struggling companies, unlike today when the aerospace industry depends on massive government spending. Shy of cash themselves, the military services looked to these firms and fledgling airlines to create new equipment. Years later, Igor I. Sikorsky would remark wryly of this period: "The greatest danger of aviation at this time was starvation."*

However grim the struggle for economic survival in the twenties and thirties there were compensations: it was also a time of much razzle-dazzle and general merriment. Aviation then was exciting and adventurous—it was an industry that had much in common with the world of show business. There was color, publicity, and news appeal, and in terms of exciting public interest the newly arrived Autogiro was in a class by itself.

Despite the depression, in the early 1930's Autogiros were

* The comment was made at a Royal Aero Club dinner in London in 1955.

22. Spectators watch a Kellett Autogiro take off from the street in front of the Department of Commerce Building in Washington on May 19, 1939, during an experimental airmail operation sponsored by Eastern Air Lines. The Kellett landed, picked up mail at a temporary post office in the Commerce Building, then flew to Washington's Hoover Airport. The flight demonstrated the possibilities of using Autogiros to link metropolitan post offices with outlying airports and helped Eastern win a contract for regular Autogiro mail service in Philadelphia, which began on July 6, 1939. The aircraft is a Kellett KD-1, powered by a 225-horsepower Jacobs engine. It cruised at about 100 miles per hour, could slow down to 25, and had a top speed of 125.

much in the headlines in the United States. The two major manufacturers were joined by another, the Buhl Aircraft Company of Detroit. In August, 1929, the first public demonstration had been made with one Cierva machine at the Cleveland Air Races; in 1930, several giros were shown, attracting much public interest. The same year, an Autogiro led an "air parade" during an airshow at Newark Airport just across the river from New York City. Later a special demonstration was given for the venerable inventor, Thomas Edison, whose helicopter experiments dated back almost fifty years. In a widely quoted statement, Edison commented: "That's the answer, that's the answer," and called the Autogiro "the greatest advance that could have been made in aviation." The next year, the Autogiro received even more publicity when veteran Pitcairn pilot Jim Ray landed one on the White House lawn—and took off again—for the ceremony at which President Herbert Hoover presented the highly prized Collier Trophy to manufacturer Harold F. Pitcairn "for the greatest achievement in aviation, the value of which has been demonstrated by actual use in the preceding year." The award was made on April 22, 1931, and during the same month famed woman pilot Amelia Earhart set a world's altitude record for Autogiros of 18,400 feet. A forward-looking newspaper, the *Detroit News*, acquired a Pitcairn Autogiro, NR 799W, which was probably the first rotating-wing aircraft in history to be operated by a newspaper.

Kindled by this activity, a wave of interest and enthusiasm spread across the country, both within aviation circles and without. Much of this was due to promotion of the Autogiro as a super-safe, easy-to-fly aircraft that signaled the age of wings for everybody. Not only would it revolutionize air transportation by providing airline access right to the city centers— an issue still being fought out with the helicopter today—but it was to be the "Family Flying Machine," a kind of aerial Ford that would put the whole country on rotating wings. As always with every new foolproof flying machine, the enthusiasm voiced was loudest from those who knew the least about flying. To the enthralled amateur, this new kind of airplane that landed with a gentle, straight-down descent, that seemingly could hover still in the air and could take off with practically no forward run, was the answer to the dream of Everyman's airplane and speeches and articles in this vein began to appear in the newspapers and magazines of the day.

Some were a fair appraisal of the rotorplane, but others were just plain foolish. Self-made experts—politicians, businessmen, editors—vied with one another in praising the giro to the skies. In a radio broadcast one United States Senator said: "Businessmen can commute from within 90 to 100 miles from the centre of the city and land on the centre of their roof . . . without being in danger . . ." Other comments by responsible citizens who might have known better called it "an airplane which can take off from the roof of a skyscraper and land on Pike's Peak," said it could make aviation a "backyard proposition," that it was easier to fly than any airplane—"one can in a pinch simply sit still and let it descend vertically without much danger."

Not that those in aviation disagreed violently. For them the vision was especially meaningful. Captain Frank Hawks, a colorful pilot in the leather breeches and silk scarf tradition, who had established many point-to-point speed-records, flew the Autogiro and thought well of it. Hawks may have been particularly aware of the virtues of the Autogiro because of his experience nursing the racers of that era to hot landings without benefit of flaps or variable-pitch propellers. He enthusiastically described his first flight at the controls of an Autogiro in an article which appeared in the *U.S. Air Services Magazine* and was quoted by Cierva in *Wings of Tomorrow*:

> The take-off in itself is effected exactly like that of an airplane. One may dive and climb at will, make vertical turns, and so on. The Autogiro flies exactly like any ordinary airplane. The real sensation that I experienced was in landing. Cutting off the motor 1,000 feet directly over the field, I pulled the stick back and proceeded to fly, on my first landing, about thirty miles an hour coming in to land. The descent was at about an angle of 45 degrees and on touching the ground I did not roll more than ten feet without any application of the wheel brakes whatsoever. I took off again and again and landed to become accustomed to this new strange craft. It intrigued and thrilled me.

I now had enough experience to attempt a more vertical descent
. . . it is quite a sensation for a pilot who has been flying a fast
airplane that lands between 60 and 70 miles an hour and that must
be manoeuvred carefully into a field, making sure his judgment of
approach is accurately managed, to step into a machine and fly
right over the centre of the field, shut off his motor and then drop
right straight down in the circle which marks the centre of airports.

Yet, despite favorable reports of this sort, some pilots had
reservations about this wonder with the whirling wings. The
nonbelievers raised any number of questions, some of them
very much to the point. What about the possibility of the bearings in the mast seizing, or the rotor blades breaking because of
the tremendous centrifugal loads? Then too, there was the
skepticism generated by the fact that in many ways, the rotorplane was a result of empirical experimentation, of successful
hunches and guesses—not of a scientific theory you could get
down in black and white. There was, for example, the ground
resonance that had showed up in the Army trials (and still gives
helicopter designers trouble today), vibration that could occur
when the rotor was turning over while the ship was still on the
ground and actually shake the machine to pieces in a few
seconds, leaving the pilot with the feeling he had been run
through a cocktail mixer.

But it would be unfair to overstress the mechanical short-
comings of the early Autogiros. The designers were stimulated
by the challenge of this new aircraft, and they worked steadily
to overcome each failing or limitation. A pattern of step-by-step
improvement emerged that ultimately would lead to the perfection of the helicopter. Looking back, we can see that the
giros of thirty years ago actually served as flying test beds for
rotor systems that eventually would be adapted to helicopters.

A major step forward in 1932 was the development of the
"direct control" rotor, which appeared on a modified Cierva
C-19, leading to the elimination of the ailerons and stub wings.
With this system the rotor was mounted on a kind of universal
joint or "rocking head" so that it could be tilted, resulting in a
force which would pull the giro in that direction. This was a
very great improvement over the airplane-type control surfaces

used on the earlier rotorplanes which depended on the airflow from forward movement, and was most noticeable in lateral control (the ability to roll the Autogiro to the right or left). With the older types at low forward speeds the blast of air driven back from the propeller helped the tail surfaces, but the ailerons were out of the slipstream from the propeller and they would become sluggish before the elevator or rudder were affected. The pilot therefore had trouble with lateral control. Since the new system worked independently of forward speed, it was considerably better. This brought the giro even closer to the ideal of being able to hover, though of course it could never really hover as long its rotor was free-wheeling and not powered. Although the elevators and the rudder were still necessary, the introduction of direct control eliminated the need for the ailerons and they—and the wings, as well—were discarded; the "wingless" Autogiro had appeared.

The next important improvement, not long in coming, was literally a leap forward into the future: In the mid-1930's a Cierva Autogiro was developed with a device intended to permit a straight-up "jump" take-off. Calculated to answer one of the Autogiro's major failings, the need for a take-off run to build up rotor speed, this moved the design of the rotorplane that much closer to the true helicopter. Eventually it proved successful, and for the first time a rotating-wing flying machine existed that could actually lift itself vertically into the air.

Seemingly a complicated system, it was actually a combination of simple mechanical devices that had been in use for years and was designed, as far as possible, to function automatically; it included a clutch and drive-shaft arrangement which connected the engine at the front with the rotor hub and thus permitted the pilot to drive the rotor under power while the aircraft was still on the ground. Another important feature was the pitch control, an early form of the collective control found on today's helicopters, which allowed the pilot to increase the pitch of the blades to an angle greater than that used for autorotation. After the desired rotor speed was reached (actually the rotor was overspeeded to build up inertia), the drive system was declutched, the pitch of the blades increased

—"pulling in pitch," as with a modern helicopter—and the Autogiro went straight up some 30 or 40 feet.

Once in the air, all the pilot had to do for forward flight was to gun the engine. The mechanism automatically flattened the pitch of the blades to the right angle for autorotation, once they had started to slow down. The business of declutching the driveshaft before taking off was important; in fact, it points up the real difference between this machine and the true helicopter. The rotor had to be disconnected from the engine before take-off because the giro had no way of counteracting torque, the twisting force from the engine that wants to turn the fuselage in the direction opposite to that in which the rotor turns. While the aircraft was sitting on the ground, the weight on the landing gear kept it from twisting, but once in the air it would have spun like a top if the power to the rotor had been continued.

Another type developed in Britain in this period, also capable of vertical take-off, was the AR III Hafner Gyroplane, first flown in 1935. The designer, Raoul Hafner, had built two experimental helicopters in his native Austria before emigrating to England in 1933. In his new country Hafner played an important role in rotating-wing developments, particularly during World War II. Unlike other giros that needed to fly forward to build up airspeed after jumping off the ground, the Hafner Gyroplane could rise and continue to climb out at a fairly steep angle in what was called a "towering take-off." This advanced machine incorporated improved forms of *collective* pitch control and *cyclic* pitch control as well, similar to the systems found on some modern helicopters.

The development of cyclic pitch control was another major step forward. Instead of "rocking" the rotor head, this approach called for *feathering*—increasing and decreasing the pitch of the blades in cycles as they turned—each blade would assume a high pitch position on one side of the rotor's circle and a low pitch on the other side. This, naturally, meant an increase in lift on one side and a decrease in lift on the other side, and thus the rotor could be inclined in the direction desired. A notable example in the United States was the promising Wil-

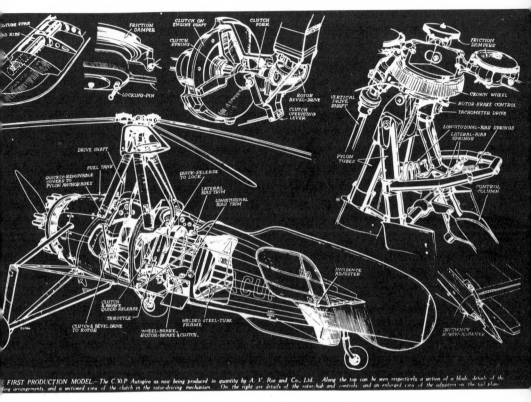

FIRST PRODUCTION MODEL.— *The C.30.P. Autogiro as now being produced in quantity by A. V. Roe and Co., Ltd. Along the top can be seen respectively a section of a blade, details of the ing arrangements, and a sectioned view of the clutch in the rotor-driving mechanism. On the right are details of the rotor hub and controls, and an enlarged view of the adjusters on the tail plane.*

23. This drawing, which appeared in the August 1, 1934, issue of the British magazine, The Aeroplane, shows details of a wingless Cierva "jump take-off", Autogiro, the C-30. The rotor was oversped on the ground through a mechanical drive system from the engine, the pitch angle of the blades was increased to provide the necessary lift, and simultaneously the drive system was declutched. The aircraft then climbed into the air powered only by the inertia of the rotor; this eliminated any problem of torque reaction from the engine. Once in the air, the blades flattened out to the correct pitch for autorotation. Of the various technical details, the uncovered section of a rotor blade at the upper left is particularly interesting for its similarity to the helicopter blades that came later.

ford Gyroplane, developed by E. Burke Wilford near Phila-delphia; it was one of the advanced types tested by the Navy before World War II, built under a government research and development contract.* Much of its development was based on the ideas of two German experimenters, Walter Rieseler and Walter Kreiser (sensible mechanics, not engineers) brought to the U.S. by Wilford in 1930. The design was unique in other ways: besides having a practical blade feathering system for cyclic control, it also introduced a *rigid rotor* (sometimes called a "hingeless" rotor) that worked. In this system there were no hinges to allow the blades to flap up and down as they turned. Instead, the feathering ability of the blades was utilized—through a camming system—to change their pitch as they rotated, thus equalizing the lift as each blade advanced forward and then retreated away from the airflow from the front (a further explanation of rigid rotor systems is provided in Chap-ter IX). Designed with a lifting wing as well as a rotor, another feature of the Wilford Gyroplane was the fact that it could fly with much of the lift coming from the wing. An early version of the Gyroplane flew in 1931; eventually it was developed into the Navy's XOZ-1, which flew beautifully in 1937.

Ironically, these various improvements to the giro signaled the end of its superiority in the rotating-wing field. The brilliant, intuitive research and plain hard work that had perfected the machine had also led to the very threshold of the age of the helicopter. All the important spadework had been accom-plished: the principle of autorotation, efficient and reliable rotor blades, highly perfected rotor heads, the control of rotor pitch, and experience with powered rotors. The helicopter pioneers, many working almost independently of the rotor-plane, suddenly realized that the path was clear.

By a strange twist of history, a completely independent type of aircraft, thought by some to be a freak, had been steadily

---

* Financially independent, E. Burke Wilford was—and still is—an aviation experimenter, designer and enthusiast in the tradition of Sir George Cayley and Juan de la Cierva. Besides his own work in the development of the rigid rotor Gyroplane, Wilford's efforts stimulated thinking of others in Philadelphia area before World War II (then the center of U.S. rotating-wing activity); in his own words, he was a "technical counter-irritant."

24. *The Convertoplane, cross between an airplane and a rotorplane, was developed in the United States in the 1930's by the "father of the convertoplane," inventor Gerard P. Herrick, aided by Ralph H. McClarren of Philadelphia's Franklin Institute. Basically, the design was a biplane with an upper wing that could function either as a lifting surface or as a two-bladed teetering rotor. Flown by test pilot George Townsend in 1937, the aircraft demonstrated successful conversions in flight from a biplane to a rotorplane. Herrick was striving for an aircraft that could achieve speed as an airplane while possessing ability to convert to rotating-wing configuration for landing and take-off in tight areas. The idea of "convertible" aircraft still beguiles helicopter designers today.*

25. *A little-known rotating-wing development during World War II was the Fa-330 autorotative kite built by Focke-Achgelis to be flown from decks of German submarines as a one-man observation platform. Actually a glider with a three-bladed rotor, it needed a minimum airspeed of 17 miles per hour to be towed aloft, and the U-boat had to run along the surface into the wind to create the airflow. Several of the kites, fitted with wheel undercarriages, were towed behind Storch observation planes for pilot training. Since the war a number of tiny rotorplane gliders, "rotor kites" with simplified control systems, have been built in the United States and Britain similar to the Fa-330, and some have been fitted with small engines and propellers.*

modified and improved until it was ready to blend with the rapidly developing helicopter. By the mid-1930's the first true helicopters were taking to the air, designed with rotors and other components that were derived from the giros. The pressure of wartime experimentation soon accelerated this growth, and the rotorplane eventually faded into the background, remembered for the most part in the public mind, only as the Spanish windmill plane.

After World War II there was some revival of interest. In order to overcome the inherent limitation on the top speed of the helicopter, aircraft termed "compound helicopters" have appeared that incorporate features of the earlier rotorplanes. These aircraft can take off straight up with the rotor under power and then can convert, in flight, to freewheeling in order to fly faster. Still other types of rotorcraft have been built in the last ten or fifteen years that are nothing more than modern adaptations of the giros of the 1920's and 1930's. As history repeats itself, some have even been proclaimed as new family cars of the air.

It is difficult to say where this narrative should end; in various forms the rotorplane is still with us today, and it may have a more important role to play in the future. But there was an ending, of sorts, to the story of the Spanish windmill plane. In December, 1936, the year of success for the Bréguet-Dorand helicopter, Juan de la Cierva—who had striven for so long to make low-speed flight safe—was killed in the fiery crash of an airliner groping its way through a fog at London's Croydon Airport.

III

The Coming of Age

"*Mais, en ce qui concerne la déscente, nous comptions beaucoup sur l'experimentation, car nos calculs étaient encore assez imprécis.*" (*But in that which concerned the descent, we counted much on experimentation, since our calculations were yet too imprecise.*)
—Maurice Claisse, test pilot for the Bréguet-Dorand helicopter, commenting on a flight in September, 1936.
"*We built the first helicopter by what we hoped was intelligent guess. It was time of crystal ball.*"
—Professor Igor Alexis Sikorsky, Chief Aerodynamicist, Sikorsky Aircraft, concerning the VS-300 helicopter of 1939.

By the middle 1930's those engaged in the merry-go-round of rotating-wing research realized that the age of the helicopter was close at hand. It had to be. Much of the theory was known; even the actual components existed in one form or another, due in part to the intensive work that had gone into the perfection of the Autogiros and Gyroplanes.

From the rotorplanes, and from the few imperfect helicopters that had flown, the intricacies of rotor system design had been learned, as well as the art of building light, strong, and flexible blades. Designers knew how—by flapping or feathering—to overcome the unequal lift forces caused by the blades rushing at, and then moving away from, the airflow coming from the front when the aircraft was in forward flight. They also knew how to control the pitch of the blades collectively, so all could increase their pitch simultaneously, in order to rise straight up. And of course the ability of the Autogiro's blades to turn in autorotation, without power, pointed the way to a safety feature that would permit a helicopter with engine failure to glide down safely.

More difficult was the problem of controlling the rotor pitch so the aircraft could be moved in the horizontal plane. Helicopter experimenters and giro designers, as well, had shown the way with various ways of accomplishing cyclic pitch control. One method, as described in Chapter II, was "feathering," the use of an elaborate mechanical linkage that increased the pitch in cycles so that each blade, as it swept around, would bite a little more in one part of the disc of rotation (and a little less on the opposite side) so the rotor would "lean over" and pull in that direction.*

There was even a store of knowledge available on the problem of driving the rotor under power. The later-model Autogiros were one source, since these aircraft were equipped with an engine-driven "jump system" mechanism for the rotor that could hop the machine straight up into the air.

With so much already accomplished, what then was holding up the creation of a truly successful helicopter? If we overlook the question of finances (the resurgence of world militarism and the impending war would soon take care of that), for the most part there remained only the problem of blending these elements together correctly, perhaps more by intuitive engineering than by science. Although important problems remained to be solved, the solutions, theoretically at least, were available.

One problem has been that old and persistent devil, torque. At the same time that an engine is striving to turn the rotor in one direction it will, not unreasonably, try to turn the fuselage of the helicopter in the opposite direction; this, as we have

---

* There were other methods that had the same effect. One was a system for "rocking" the entire rotor hub by mounting it on a universal joint which allowed the hub to be tilted in any direction.

seen, is the torque reaction. Uncontrolled in some early helicopters, it could produce an embarrassing and even hilarious effect—the rotor would turn one way, the ship and the pilot went the other. Theoretically, there were ways to cope with this: two rotors could turn in opposite directions on the same mast so the twisting forces canceled out; another method called for the use of an auxiliary rotor pulling sideways. But translating these abstract theories into mechanical reality was something else again; nevertheless, by the early 1930's torque was fairly well under control, as well as the other problems associated with the design of the rotor drive systems.

The experimenters were more concerned with problems that had to do with actual flight characteristics, for helicopters were now flying regularly, after a fashion; that is, they were hovering and flying at slow speeds in horizontal movement over the ground and were even climbing straight up to considerable heights. But there were still many deficiencies: vibration, unreliability in the mechanisms, and a worrisome lack of control and stability. Still another problem was the need for rotor systems that would permit freewheeling in case of engine failure, so that autorotational emergency landings could be made. Another important goal that had not been reached in the early 1930's was the ability to reach high speeds in forward flight; many of the experimental machines of the period traveled no faster than a man could run.

The mechanisms for overcoming these obstacles existed, in one form or another, and it remained for some one designer to put all the pieces of the puzzle together in the right combination. When a really successful helicopter appeared, it would identify itself by having all the necessary virtues in one package —stability, control, speed, lack of vibration, and other such impressive characteristics.

The first successful helicopters, machines that could accomplish to some degree all the things we expect of a helicopter today, began to take to the air a few years before World War II, in 1935 and 1936. The pattern of development paralleled the early days of the airplane; it, too, had come of age just before a global war.

In the thirties, with the rise of Hitler and the threat of a second war, history began to repeat itself. Aeronautical research and design was stimulated, and from this surge of activity came a whole witch's brew of new war planes; low-wing monoplane fighters with closed cockpits and retractable landing gear, heavily armed bombers of like design, and specialized attack planes such as the German *Stuka* dive bomber. But the bubbling cauldron also produced one seemingly peaceful bird, the helicopter, which had no immediate use as a weapon.

At this point it must be said that there was really no one inventor of the helicopter. Independent research and development was going on throughout the 1930's, more or less simultaneously, in various countries. To mention just a few, the experimenters included Igor I. Sikorsky in the United States, Raoul Hafner and C. G. Pullin in Britain, a team—Louis Bréguet and René Dorand—in France, E. H. Henrich Focke and Anton Flettner in Germany, and Boris N. Yuriev, Ivan P. Bratukhin, and Nikolai I. Kamov (a student of Bratukhin) in the Soviet Union. To say whose machine was the first is difficult, to say the least. In the early thirties some helicopters had already flown clear of the ground, but this was hardly proof in itself of a successful aircraft, and the argument goes on to this day. However, if a close examination is made of exactly what was accomplished, and *when,* by the two leading European competitors—one German, the other French—the picture becomes clearer.

There is a widespread notion, even within the aviation industry itself, that the world's first flyable helicopter was the widely publicized Focke-Achgelis Fa-61 that set a number of world's records in Germany in 1937. To demonstate its control and maneuverability, this machine was flown indoors in a Berlin sports arena by a woman pilot, and photos of this performance appeared in magazines and newspapers throughout the world.

But the first successful machine to fly in Europe—and, almost certainly, in the world—was French not German. One of the two designers was Louis Bréguet, the same determined pioneer who had created the very first rotating-wing contraption to lift a man from the ground in the year of 1907. Stymied then in his attempt to build a practical helicopter, Bréguet—like Igor I. Sikorsky—turned to fixed-wing airplanes and established a new company; during World War I the name of Bréguet had ranked with the names of the other great war planes of the era.

On June 26, 1935, this French helicopter—the Bréguet-Dorand "Gyroplane Laboratoire"—created by Bréguet with co-designer René Dorand, took to the air with little fanfare. The machine was complicated, powered by a massive (for the day) 420-horsepower *Hispano-Wright* engine. It had two rotors turn-in opposite directions, mounted coaxially one above the other on the same mast, with the two drive shafts turning one *inside* the other. Stemming from this configuration was the need for a large clearance between the upper and lower rotors, to ensure that the blades would not collide as they flexed up and down. The first flights were not altogether satisfactory, with insufficient stability shown while hovering. But the designers persevered with bit-by-bit improvement in the classic pattern. Control was adequate; within a month Bréguet was able to take off, go into forward flight, circle over the spot, and then return for a landing. On December 22, 1935, six months before the first short hop of the Fa-61, the Bréguet-Dorand established a Fédération Aeronautique Internationale speed record, significantly, of 67 miles per hour. Other helicopters had flown before that had shown some height and endurance, but the "Gyroplane Laboratoire" was the first to demonstrate, for F.A.I. record, an impressive forward speed coupled with good control characteristics. The next flight for the F.A.I. was made nine months later, on September 22, 1936, when an altitude record of 517 feet was established. This was followed by two more records on November 24, 1936: a duration of over one hour and two minutes, and a closed-circuit distance record of 27.4 miles.

The complex coaxial rotors of the Bréguet-Dorand incorporated, in one form or another, mechanisms that solved the problems that had vexed the earlier experimenters. The two rotors turned in opposite directions, thus canceling out torque. The long slender blades (rotor diameter was a large 54 feet) were secured to a hinged *articulated* hub that let each blade flap

26. Successful Bréguet-Dorand "Gyroplane Laboratoire" flew on June 26, 1935. A coaxial design weighing 4,500 pounds, it had twin rotors turning in opposite directions on the same mast. After further development, the aircraft established world's speed, altitude and endurance records. The pilot, barely visible here, sat within the fuselage frame behind the rotor transmission and mast. With Maurice Claisse as test pilot, this helicopter was flown up to the outbreak of World War II.

27. *Flown on June 26, 1936, the Focke-Achgelis Fa-61 put the
Germans squarely in the lead. The aircraft weighed some 2,100
pounds and was powered by a 160-horsepower Bramo radial engine
mounted airplane-fashion at the front of the fuselage (the engine was
cooled by a small wooden propeller, cut down to the diameter of the
cylinders), which drove two three-bladed rotors mounted on outriggers, one on each side of the fuselage. To demonstrate its controllability, the Fa-61 was flown indoors.*

up and down to compensate for dissymetry of lift. A *cyclic pitch control* system was provided, whereby the pitch angle of each blade could be varied as it turned; the blade could ride high in one point in the disc of rotation and low on the opposite side, thus inclining the ship—it could be rolled to either side or nosed up or down. (To go into forward flight the nose went down, and the rotors were then propelling the aircraft forward as well as providing the lift.) The pilot also had a *collective pitch control* system for rising vertically—the pitch of all the blades could be increased or decreased, by an equal amount, simultaneously. Finally, to "yaw" the helicopter (turn to the right or left) there was a *differential collective* system—the collective pitch in one of the two rotors could be increased over the other; the increased resistance meant more torque in one rotor than the other, and the ship would then turn around on its vertical axis.

The performance of the French helicopter is all the more impressive when compared with the existing F.A.I. records and serves to illustrate how much of an advance had been achieved by the Bréguet-Dorand. The previous record (mentioned in Chapter I) dated from October of 1930, when the Italian helicopter designed by Corradino d'Ascanio and flown by Marinello Nelli (it too was a coaxial machine), stayed aloft for a duration of eight minutes and forty-five seconds, flew a distance of 3,538 feet, and rose to a height of 59 feet.

However, what would prove to be a more efficient helicopter was by now flying in Germany. Featuring two side-by-side rotors positioned on outriggers projecting from an airplane-type fuselage, the Focke-Achgelis Fa-61 hopped into the air on June 26, 1936, with test pilot Ewald Rohlfs at the controls. This first flight lasted only twenty-eight seconds; oddly, it was made exactly one year to the day after the first flight of the Bréguet-Dorand. The Fa-61 was rapidly perfected; in May of 1937 the first autorotational landing was made—an important breakthrough.* In June of that year it established

---

* In 1937 the Bréguet helicopter as well was modified for autorotational flight with the incorporation of a constant-speed unit for its rotor, and landings in autorotation were made.

many new records, including a speed of 77 miles per hour and an altitude of 7,800 feet. More record-breaking flights followed, lengthy cross-country trips were made, and the Fa-61 was duly certificated and put on the German register as an "approved" aircraft—the first helicopter in history to be so recognized. The indoor flights were made during February of 1938 in the Deutschlandhalle in Berlin, dramatizing the ease of handling, particularly the excellent lateral control inherent to the side-by-side arrangement of the rotors.

In performance, general reliability, and degree of perfection the Fa-61 was regarded as superior to the Bréguet-Dorand. Accordingly, the Focke aircraft is frequently given credit as being the world's first "practical" helicopter, and the 1935 achievements of the French designers are overlooked. But this line of reasoning fails to consider that the Bréguet-Dorand copter itself was an even more extraordinary improvement over what had gone before—so much so that it represented a very great breakthrough. In the matter of forward speed in particular, the French aircraft moved the top speed of helicopters from a pace scarcely faster than that at which a man could run to a very respectable 67 miles per hour. The Bréguet-Dorand helicopter, incidentally, was constructed much earlier than its competitor, in the years 1930-1933. In fact the first attempt at flight, which ended in a crash due to faulty control, was made in November of 1933. After establishing F.A.I. records in 1935 and 1936, the development of this helicopter continued up to the beginning of the war, with Maurice Claisse as the test pilot. It was destroyed during the course of an Allied raid on the Villacoublay air base where it had been stored, in 1943.

The Fa-61 was the special creation of Professor E. H. Henrich Focke, formerly the design chief of an established firm that bore his name, Focke-Wulf, who had been displaced by the Nazis as being "politically unsafe." The professor promptly started a small new company—Focke-Achgelis—devoted to the perfection of rotating-wing aircraft, a subject in which he was strongly interested. His company had a license agreement with Cierva to build Autogiros—the first was a Cierva C-19—and the Autogiro influence was evident in the Fa-61. Apparently Focke buried himself in his work and the Nazis left him alone, though eventually he was involved in work for the military. Professor Focke's side-by-side rotor configuration set the style for several types that were developed in Germany during the war.

German pre-eminence was not limited to the designs of Professor Focke. Between 1938 and 1940 another outstanding German aeronautical engineer, Anton Flettner (his experiments dated back to 1932) produced a radical new machine that would be developed into the best helicopter of World War II. This was what would later be called a "synchropter," a machine previously suggested by Dr. James A. J. Bennett of the English Cierva Company which Flettner nursed into a practical aircraft. It was a design that raised the collective eyebrows of aircraft designers throughout the world.

The machine had two rotors, set so closely together that the blades were closely intermeshed. An important requirement was that the drive system had to synchronize closely so the blades would not collide—hence the name. In fact, during the early stages of development there was an accident in which a test pilot was killed when somehow the system got out of whack and the blades came together in flight, shearing the rotors right down to the hubs. Eventually the machine was perfected, and in the final production configuration the two hubs were only 2 feet apart, though of course they were angled out to the right and left away from each other so there was room for the blades to rotate.

These two basic types, the Focke-Achgelis with two side-by-side rotors and the Fletner with its dual rotors intermeshing in eggbeater fashion, were the basic designs pursued by the Germans during the war. Both types were improved to the point where they completely overshadowed anything built on the Allied side.

The emergence of the wartime Focke-Achgelis and the Flettner Helicopters as highly perfected military aircraft startled the rest of the aviation world, although in most quarters outside

the industry the significance of these achievements was not
fully appreciated. In rotating-wing activity the Germans had
seemed late-comers; for example, no large manufacturer in that
country had shown any real interest in the Autogiro during the
years of its birth in the 1920's. Yet suddenly they had broken
into the clear, outpacing all competition. Though the reasons
for this were complex, they were not mysterious.

With a deliberate sense of the dramatic, in 1935 Hitler had
suddenly unveiled the existence of a powerful new *Luftwaffe*,
and Europe began to realize the true implications of the red
and black swastika flag. Supported by a government that
proved to be nothing more than a political structure for a death
machine that destroyed millions of innocent people, the German aviation industry was rushed into a program of arming
the Nazi Air Force with the newest tools of air warfare.

In Britain and France there was a sudden desperate aware-
ness that they were no longer on top. In Britain, where the
menace had long been ignored (though not by Winston
Churchill), the Royal Air Force, still equipped in the main
with biplane fighters, began hurriedly to re-equip and expand.
In France, a disorganized aviation industry was nationalized
in an effort to increase production; and the result was an immediate slump. In the Allied nations this sudden effort to produce
modern aircraft caused rotating-wing research, which had been
proceeding at a steady but leisurely pace, to be put aside in
favor of more pressing matters.

In Germany things were different. There the build-up had
been steady and deliberate. The Germans, denied military
aircraft by the restrictions of the Treaty of Versailles, had
started to create a clandestine air arm in the 1920's even before
Hitler came to power. Airplanes were built for Germany in
other countries; the notorious *Stuka* Ju-87 dive bomber was
evolved mainly from the work of the Swedish subsidiary of
the Junkers Company. "Civilian" airliners and sport planes built
at home by Dornier and Heinkel displayed characteristics that
were plainly military. Both Lufthansa, the national airline, and
private flying clubs were utilized to train pilots for the new
Luftwaffe. And of all the paradoxes of that nightmarish era,

there was the secret agreement under which the pilots of the new *Luftwaffe* were trained in Soviet Russia.*

This drive for a new air force second to none meant that inevitably some of the funds would filter down to such esoteric projects as the Focke-Achgelis and Flettner helicopters. Drawing upon every available source of information, supported by military contracts, with an industrial base that has rarely been surpassed for technical excellence, it is not surprising that German rotorcraft soon led the world.

In the late 1930's the performance of the Focke-Achgelis machine with its side-by-side rotors was so much superior to the coaxial Bréguet it seemed that the German design would dominate the field for years to come. This view was reinforced by the fact that the Fa-61 was quickly followed by other helicopters with twin rotors mounted in a similar arrangement. One was the British Weir W-5, designed by C. G. Pullin, first flown by his son, Raymond A. Pullin, in Scotland in June 1938†; the other was the experimental Platt-LePage XR-1, built for the U.S. Army and flown in this country in July, 1940. Two other noteworthy types followed that were designed with this same side-by-side arrangement for twin rotors; one was Russian, the other American. Both, incidentally, were twin-engine aircraft, the earliest successful multi-engine helicopters to take to the air.

The Russians were first with the TsAGI *Omega*, designed by Professor Ivan P. Bratukhin, powered by M-11 radial engines of 140 horsepower each, and test flown in 1941. However, it was not until after the end of the war that the machine was improved and refined into a serviceable aircraft, the *Omega II*, described in some detail later in this chapter.

* According to the official history of the British Royal Air Force in World War II (Volume I: *The Fight at Odds*), a clandestine flying school for German Army officers was opened at Lipezk, Russia, which produced pilots, observers, and air gunners. The school was operational from the period 1928-1931 and trained many of the officers who led the new German Air Force.

† The British industrialist James G. Weir was instrumental in bringing the Autogiro pioneer Juan de la Cierva to England, and his company was foremost in rotating-wing development in that country. Weir was primarily interested in the safe, low-speed flight characteristics of the Autogiro for popular flying; nevertheless his organization perfected the helicopter in Britain. The W-5 was followed by a larger helicopter, the W-6.

28. *This Soviet twin-rotor, twin-engine* Omega I, *with laterally mounted rotors resembles the smaller Focke-Achgelis Fa-61. Design work began in 1939 by Ivan P. Bratukhin, and the aircraft was first flown in 1941, powered by two radial engines. Development ceased during the war, but the aircraft was shown at the Tushino air show in 1946 and was reported as in limited production. A larger, improved version followed in 1948.*

The other twin-engined, side-by-side rotor machine was the McDonnell XHJD-1, developed for the U.S. Navy. First flown only after the end of the war, in February of 1946, it seems to have been a direct descendant of the Platt-LePage XR-1. This one and only model of the XHJD-1 flew for the U.S. Navy for a number of years as a research vehicle. Powered by two 450-horsepower Pratt and Whitney radial engines, the McDonnell machine was slightly larger than the Russian helicopter and was intended to carry ten passengers, its fully loaded weight being 11,500 pounds. Though the design was not carried further, the XHJD-1 proved a useful research tool. The success of Professor Focke, of course, was behind this activity in side-by-side rotors (it has been suggested that there are fashions in aircraft as in women's hats).

The excellent performance of the Fa-61 with its two side-by-side rotors led the Focke-Achgelis firm to continue this line of development throughout the war. Hard on the heels of this successful little single-seater, they began to build a six-passenger machine, the Fa-266, for Lufthansa. Externally at least, this aircraft appeared to be nothing more than a scaled-up version of the Fa-61.

The scope of the German rotating-wing effort during the war was so wide that it is only possible to deal with the more important developments, such as the Fa-266. But in a sense, the career of this machine—the world's first transport helicopter —is almost symbolic. It serves to illustrate how the Germans sought to create superior new air weapons, helicopters and jet airplanes alike, while their industry was under intensive aerial bombardment. A British intelligence report published after the war* had this to say about the Fa-266, redesignated, in the military version, as the Fa-223:

> The first prototype was completed in 1939 shortly after the outbreak of war. It was then decided to develop it for military purposes and, after 100 hours of ground running and hovering on

* The source for this quotation is *British Intelligence Objectives Sub-Committee Overall Report No. 8, Rotating Wing Activities in Germany during the period 1939-1945.* Permission for the use of this material, as well as the three illustrations appearing in the text, is by courtesy of the Controller of Her Britannic Majesty's Stationery Office.

29. Shown in British Royal Air Force insignia is a German Focke-Achgelis Fa-223, the largest helicopter actually in production during World War II. Powered by a 1,000-horsepower engine, the Fa-223 was a twin-rotor machine designed to carry six passengers. Only three flyable Fa-223's survived at war's end, and in September of 1945 one of these was flown to Britain, the first helicopter to cross the English Channel.

ropes, it finally emerged with the new type number Fa 223 in August, 1940, when the first free flight was made. It was not until early in 1942 that the type was considered to be ready for use by the armed forces and official trials were made.

A production series of 100 was then started, but until July, 1942, only two aircraft were put into the air, ten others in the process of manufacture being destroyed in a bombing raid. The firm were then evacuated to South Germany, but only eight additional aircraft were test flown. Six of these and all others which were being assembled were destroyed in another air attack in July, 1944. Although another production line was started in Berlin with the aim of delivering 400 aircraft per month, only one further aircraft was actually completed before the occupation.

On cessation of hostilities there were three aircraft in existence, one of which was destroyed by its pilot. Of the other two, one was flown by its German crew to the Airborne Forces Experimental Establishment [in England] in September, 1945, having made the first crossing of the English Channel by helicopter. Unfortunately, it was destroyed before its characteristics could be established, when the failure of an auxiliary drive caused an automatic change to the autorotative condition during a trial flight. As the change occurred in a vertical ascent at approximately 60 feet from the ground, it was impossible to obtain the forward speed necessary for an autorotative landing; the aircraft was completely wrecked.

Professor Focke had been hopefully intending the Fa-266 as a genuine civilian transport, but the uses planned for the *Luftwaffe* version included troop-carrying and every other military function that helicopters have performed in recent years. Fitted with a machine gun and bombs, the Fa-223 could play anti-submarine and armed reconnaissance roles. A winch was fitted with a floating cradle for air-sea rescue operations, and a cable with quick-release mechanism below the fuselage for cargo transport as a flying crane.* Transporting supplies for mountain troops was also expected of the Fa-223, and toward the end of the war there were rumors that this highly advanced machine was to play a prominent role in the scheme for a last-ditch Nazi stronghold in the Alps.

Considering that its first flight was made in 1940 and that production began in 1942, it can be said that the six-passenger Fa-223 was almost ten years before its time. The specifications on this remarkable helicopter are enlightening: powered by a 1,000-horsepower Bramo radial engine, the production ship had an all-up weight of 10,000 pounds and could carry a maximum useful load of 2,000 pounds at 115 miles per hour. Its ceiling, when lightly loaded, was 23,400 feet. Each rotor measured 39.4 feet in diameter. Perhaps even more impressive were the excellent control characteristics and smoothness of handling: Professor Focke noted that during the mountain tests he could fly the Fa-223 with ease with his fingertips on the control stick, a performance not easily duplicated with a large helicopter today. During these mountain trials, loads of up to 2,000 pounds were carried on a cable slung below the fuselage.

An even more ambitious machine planned, though never flown, by Focke-Achgelis, during the war carried the twin-rotor side-by-side approach still further. This was the very large Fa-284, a true flying crane and more than likely the first

*A particularly advanced feature was the quick-release mechanism at the end of the cargo cable. It was operated electrically by the pilot so he could off-load without requiring help from men on the ground.

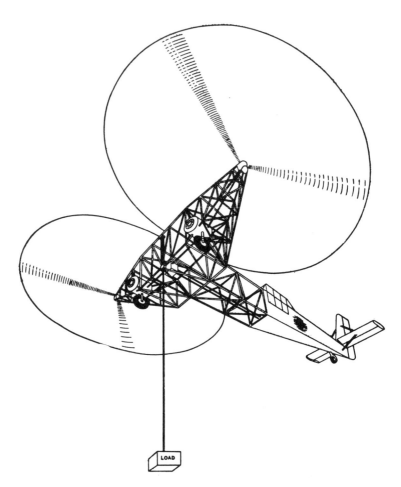

30. *The largest helicopter designed during World War II was this twin-rotor Focke-Achgelis Fa-284, a huge flying crane intended to haul such loads as armored vehicles and trucks. Some work on the Fa-284 was carried out by Bréguet, the pioneer helicopter company in France, during the German occupation. In the face of wartime difficulties the project was eventually dropped, but not before considerable design work and some airframe construction had been accomplished. The diameter of each rotor was 58.5 feet. Initially the machine was to have two B.M.W. 1,600-horsepower engines, later raised to 2,000 horsepower.*

31. *The Flettner Fl-282, shown here in United States insignia, was an advanced German helicopter used during World War II. A small and highly maneuverable machine, it featured twin rotors that were mounted offset side by side. The two rotor masts were angled out slightly to each side to permit the rotors to mesh together. Intended for operation from shipboard, trials were flown in the Baltic from the cruiser Koln, and Fl-282's were later used for convoy patrol.*

helicopter to be designed specifically for this use; it was an enormous twin-engine machine whose over-all span would have been well over 100 feet. It was expected that the ultimate design weight in the crane configuration would be 16 metric tons, and that of this no less than 7 metric tons (over 8 U.S. tons) would be pure payload.

Another major effort by the Germans during the war, perhaps more significant, was the highly-successful Flettner Fl-282 *Kolibri*, the small, two-seat, twin-rotor synchropter that was unquestionably the best helicopter of the day (The German word *"Kolibri"* means "hummingbird"). Reliable and extremely maneuverable, one of the uses intended for the Fl-282 was operations with the German Navy. According to a postwar report,* it was actually flown from landing platforms aboard ship and used for the protection of Axis convoys in the Aegean Sea. Flettner claimed that this machine was so superior to the Focke-Achgelis Fa-61 that, despite the fact both had the same engine (a 140-horsepower Siemens-Halske), his synchropter could easily climb with three people aboard while the Focke single-seater supposedly had trouble even climbing away from ground cushion. The Flettner intermesher does seem to have been superior, yet the comparison was hardly valid. The Focke Fa-61 dated from 1936 and was already obsolete during the first years of the war, while the first Fl-282 did not fly until 1940 or possibly later. It was actually a "second generation" aircraft based on the earlier Fl-265, which Flettner had used to develop his concept of intermeshing, synchronized rotors.

In 1941 the single-seater Fl-265 was subjected to a wide range of testing, mostly by the German Navy, which was interested in its use for antisubmarine operations; one test was rather unusual. To find out how vulnerable the helicopter would be to fighters, two experienced pilots, one flying a Messerschmitt 109 and the other a Focke-Wulf 190, made a twenty-minute attack on the Flettner aircraft with gun cameras. At the end of twenty minutes of mock combat, neither fighter

---

* British Intelligence Objectives Sub-Committee Overall Report No. 8. "Rotating Wing Activities in Germany during the period 1939-1945."

had made a single hit on the dodging, dancing, highly maneuverable synchropter.

Well aware they had the best machine of its type in the world, the Germans began an ambitious program to have a thousand Fl-282's mass-produced by the Bayerische Motorenwerke of Munich at their Eisenach plant. As with the Focke-Achgelis program, Allied bombers promptly cancelled out production, though twenty-two of the Flettner helicopters had been built by the war's end.

However, Flettner was not alone in his appreciation of the synchropter. In the United States a helicopter with intermeshing rotors, the XR-8, was built during the war for the Army Air Force by Kellett, a firm which had considerable experience in manufacturing Autogiros.* This machine flew in August, 1944. After some developmental work, the XR-8 ("X" for experimental) evolved into the postwar XR-10, which also had two intermeshing rotors. An eight-place helicopter, the XR-10 was for its day a large machine. The overall diameter of the two intermeshing rotors was 71 feet, the ship was twin-engined (two 450-horsepower Pratt and Whitneys), and gross weight was 13,500 pounds. The first and only XR-10 flew after the war, in April of 1947. Unhappily, it crashed, and development thus ceased.

During the wartime period an entirely different type of helicopter was being developed in the United States, which, despite the intensive German activity, would ultimately become the predominant design. Igor I. Sikorsky, designer of the world's first four-engined airplanes in Czarist Russia before World War I, had built his first helicopter as a student in 1909; it hadn't flown, nor had his second in 1910. Following the outbreak of the revolution, Sikorsky had emigrated, penniless, to the United States and started all over again, founding a new aircraft company that—staffed by many *émigré* Russians—produced a long

---

* The first helicopter produced by Kellett for the Army in 1940 was the experimental XR-2, which, not surprisingly, was a reworked YG-1 Autogiro. The next Kellett helicopter was the XR-3 (also of 1940 vintage); it too was a modified YG-1 which incorporated a feathering rotor system.

line of record-breaking transport airplanes. After a thirty-year
interval Igor I. Sikorsky created his third helicopter, the VS-
300, the first truly successful machine in the Western hemi-
sphere and a world-beater.

First flown as a tethered test rig by the fedora-wearing designer himself on September 14, 1939, the initial version of the
VS-300 was furnished with one main rotor and a single small
tail rotor to offset torque—the simple and classic Sikorsky configuration which remains unchanged to this day. In this respect
it resembled the barely flyable copter built by von Baumhauer
in 1929 and the unsuccessful machine Yuriev had constructed
as a student in 1912. Though the Sikorsky helicopter flew, the
control system was not perfected, particularly the tail rotor
and cyclic pitch controls, and almost two years of experimentation in the classic trial-and-error pattern followed. Eighteen
different configurations were tried, and at one point the VS-300
sported no less than three tail rotors. Perhaps the creation of
the VS-300 is best described in the words of Professor Igor
Alexis Sikorsky, chief aerodynamicist for the company and
cousin, once removed, to the designer. In 1957 he recalled: "We
built the first helicopter by what we hoped was intelligent
guess. It was time of crystal ball."

Igor I. Sikorsky's trials and tribulations with the VS-300 are
legendary in the industry. Not the least of his problems was in
convincing United Aircraft, the parent firm for Sikorsky Aircraft, that the project was worth spending money on. He once
described an incident during this time:

> Late in 1940, the VS-300 could fly reasonably well in nearly all
> directions except straight forward. . . . This trouble was so definite
> that a very competent and wise observer could detect it even in
> the many movies we took. So when our Mr. Eugene Wilson (vice-
> chairman of United Aircraft Corporation) once asked me why . . .
> I had to reply that this was one of the secondary engineering
> problems on which we were still working.

With its single tail rotor restored, the final version of the
VS-300 was flying during the spring and summer of 1941. It
soon exceeded several of the prewar records of the Focke-
Achgelis Fa-61, with which it was roughly comparable in size

32. *Igor I. Sikorsky's VS-300 was designed in the spring of 1939, built that summer, and first flown—tethered to the ground—in the fall of that year. With the ropes removed, the first free flight of the VS-300 was made on May 13, 1940, and by midsummer of the next year it had established an endurance record of one hour and thirty-two minutes. This photo shows the VS-300 in its final form, early in 1942, during a flight near the company plant at Stratford, Connecticut, with designer Sikorsky at the controls.*

33. *Wright Field, Ohio, May 18, 1942: Army rotating-wing exponent Colonel (now retired General) H. Frank Gregory congratulates Igor I. Sikorsky on the historic cross-country flight which delivered the XR-4 to the Army. Flown by pilot Charles L. Morris, the XR-4 covered the 761 miles between the Sikorsky plant in Connecticut and Wright Field in five days, with actual time in the air of sixteen hours and ten minutes. The pleased gentleman in the center is Orville Wright.*

34. *The experimental British Cierva W-9 of 1944-1945 vintage used a jet blast from a duct in the tail to counteract the torque effect of the main rotor. Another unusual feature for the day was the control system for the W-9's three-bladed rotor, a tilting rotor hub driven through a constant-velocity universal joint.*

and power. Even before the final modifications had been made to the VS-300, the company was hard at work on a production machine, the R-4, which was flown by Allied pilots during World War II.* And though the Sikorsky machine, as perfected, appeared on the scene years after the French and German designs the arrangement of one main rotor and one tail rotor was so practical that it easily became the predominant type.

The French and German machines and the work in the United States were important developments during this period, yet it would be unfair to minimize the activity in other countries, especially in Britain and the Soviet Union. A small wartime design team of the British Cierva Company, led by C. G. Pullin, proceeded to develop a single-rotor machine, the W-9, which had an unusual method of counteracting rotor torque. Instead of a small rotor at the tail, which was the prominent feature of the Sikorsky machines, the Cierva helicopter had a jet tailpipe facing to one side at the rear end of the fuselage. The exhaust flow from a turbine engine within the fuselage was intended to provide the force to overcome the rotor torque. This design approach was dropped after an accident to the aircraft during flight tests in 1946.

A British development of the one-main-rotor one-tail-rotor theme was the four-seater Bristol B-171 *Sycamore,* first flown in 1947 and the first helicopter to be awarded a Certificate of Airworthiness in that country in 1949. Designed with a long, slender, aesthetically pleasing fuselage and powered—in the final version—by a 520-horsepower Alvis Leonides engine, the *Sycamore* proved one of the most successful helicopters built in Britain after the war. The origins of this aircraft dated back

* During World War II the Sikorsky R-4 saw service with the U.S. Army, Navy, and Coast Guard and with British forces; the British called it the *Hoverfly.* Several of the early rescues accomplished by Coast Guard and U.S. Army R-4's have been narrated in Chapter IV. As for its use by the Navy, late in 1943 tests were made with an R-4 landing aboard a British merchant ship, the M. V. *Dagestan,* in Long Island Sound; the helicopter was piloted by Lt. Commander John A. Miller of the U.S. Navy with Brigadier General Frank Lowe (U.S. Army) aboard as observer. It is not clear if Navy R-4's were ever used in action against submarines. However, according to Volume 14 of an authoritative series, *The Rotary Wing Industry* (1954), edited by Eugene K. Liberatore for the Air Force, the first Atlantic convoy actually patrolled by helicopter sailed from New York on January 2, 1944, with three R-4's aboard.

35. *Two men clung desperately to a sling beneath a Bristol Sycamore helicopter during an attempted rescue from a raging flood in Maitland Australia, in February of 1955. The aircraft had successfully lifted the men from the top of a railway box where both had taken refuge, but apparently they couldn't get into the sling correctly; seconds later they lost their grip and fell, striking a high-tension line, and were swept away.*

to 1944 when the Bristol Aeroplane Company absorbed the Hafner Gyroplane organization (mentioned in Chapter II) and Raoul Hafner, with members of his design group, began planning the Bristol type 171. Capable of a top speed of 127 miles per hour and a cruising speed of 91, the versatile *Sycamore* went into service with the British, Belgian, Australian, and West German forces, and some are still operational today.

In Russia, as was mentioned previously, the Soviets had flown their twin-rotor *Omega I*—which had side-by-side rotors similar to the Focke designs—as early as 1941. Apparently the world's first successful twin-engined helicopter, the *Omega I* was developed into the *Omega II*, a large machine intended to carry seven passengers and a two-man crew, powered by two ASh-21 7-cylinder radial engines of approximately 800 total horsepower. This improved version (the *Omega II*) was not flown until 1948. Thereafter the machine was only in limited production and apparently was not further developed.

In 1953 there were a few accounts in the West of a newer and much larger *Omega* by Bratukhin's design team. This was the *Omega III*, which the Russians claimed as the largest helicopter in the world at that time. Powered by two ASh-90 18-cylinder radial engines (similar to the Wright *Cyclone Duplex*) rated at 2,000 horsepower each, it could carry thirty-two passengers and had a top speed, reportedly, of 128.7 miles per hour. The configuration was basically the same as the earlier model; two laterally positioned rotors and an airplane- type tail with horizontal and vertical surfaces. One of the interesting features of both the *II* and *III* was the small stub wing projecting from each side of the fuselage, upon which the rotor pylons were mounted. The first wartime *Omega* had a bare, uncovered framework to support its twin rotors and these wings seemed a natural development, resulting from the enclosing and streamlining of this structure.

After a lapse of eight years, in 1961 the Soviets revealed another side-by-side twin-rotor aircraft, the huge Kamov-designed *Vintokrulya* compound helicopter or "convertiplane," which displayed other external features as well—a lifting wing and an airplane-type tail—that seemed to indicate *Omega*

36. *Sporting an extra-wide landing gear as proof against rolling over, the experimental Model 30 is flight-tested at the Bell Helicopter Company project, Gardenville, New York, during the summer of 1943. With a configuration of one lifting rotor and one tail rotor, the Model 30 pioneered a new rotor system, with only two blades, and was the direct ancestor of a long line of successful helicopters since built by Bell. To demonstrate the effectiveness of its control system, the Model 30 was flown inside the 65th Regiment Armory in Buffalo on May 10, 1944.*

lineage. This remarkable aircraft, together with other compound helicopter types, is described in greater detail later in this chapter.

The evolution of the *Omega* was typical of much of the work in various countries in the postwar period as improvements were made to basic types that had been created just before and during the war. In the United States, in addition to Sikorsky, two notable developments of the one-main-rotor and one-tail-rotor approach were the two-place machines built by the Bell Helicopter Company and the Hiller Aircraft Company; both led to long, successful lines of small and versatile aircraft. The Bell copter, one of the first with a rotor that had only two blades, was developed, it is said, by its inventor, Arthur Young, working in a barn near Paoli, Pennsylvania (during the 1930's this part of Pennsylvania had been the center of Autogiro activity in the United States), and had the distinction of being the first to acquire an American certificate of airworthiness, thus being pronounced fit for commercial operations. The Hiller Company had its origins in the coaxial XH-44 flown by its nineteen-year-old designer, Stanley Hiller, at the University of California in 1944. In 1946 the youthful inventor turned to the single-main-rotor configuration, and on October 14, 1948, his Model 360 was awarded an airworthiness certificate. Both the Bell and Hiller helicopters were used extensively in the Korean War.

In addition to the side-by-side twin-rotor and the one-main-rotor and one-tail-rotor arrangements, the postwar era saw further development of at least three other basic types. One was the tandem twin-rotor, with one rotor positioned behind the other, perfected by Frank N. Piasecki. Another was the coaxial, two rotors on the same mast turning in opposite directions, such as the Russian Kamov and the American Gyrodyne; these can be thought of as lineal descendants of the Bréguet-Dorand machine of 1935. A third type was the twin-rotor intermeshing configuration similar to the wartime Flettner designs, manufactured primarily in the United States by Kaman Aircraft. Tracing the development of these primary types provides a broad view of the intensive helicopter research in the decade

37. On a California afternoon in 1946, twenty-two-year-old Stanley Hiller is at the controls of his stripped-down coaxial Commuter, testing a new roter system, just before a crack-up that wrecked the aircraft. Fortunately, neither Hiller nor his mechanic, Smitty Petit—whose right leg dangles free of the airframe—were hurt in the crash. Hiller had flown his first experimental helicopter, also a coaxial type, in May of 1944. During the postwar period there were nearly three hundred helicopter enterprises and most went down the drain, but Hiller went on to produce a series of successful aircraft.

after the war. If the effort during this period was particularly intense it was due to any number of reasons: the fact it was thought by many that "the age of the helicopter" was right around the corner, the availability of valuable wartime research, and perhaps most important, the stimulus of the cold war and the Korean conflict.

The wartime period has seen the creation of helicopters that could really fly. But for the most part these machines were limited in usefulness, and the next step was to create a new generation of working aircraft with greater speed, range, reliability, and other such highly desirable characteristics. Any number of configurations were tried; many were nothing more than an attempt to improve on the dominant Sikorsky approach of one main rotor on top and one small rotor at the tail. Some designers wanted to get rid of that little tail rotor—which they considered a useless appendage—in favor of other methods of torque control; perhaps a return to the idea of two (or more) smaller overhead rotors was the answer, especially for the larger transport types the young and struggling industry was hoping would soon fill the skies.

An important new design in this direction was the large ten-place tandem twin-rotor machine developed by Frank N. Piasecki for the U.S. Navy under a war-time contract. Designated as the XHRP-1, it flew at Morton, Pennsylvania, in March, 1945, the first successful design of this type in the world, and proved a more efficient approach to the twin-rotor concept than side-by-side rotors. Eventually this configuration was widely adopted, generally for heavier twin-engine transports. Among its advantages, at the time, was the small frontal area—thus reducing air resistance—and the fact that the center of gravity was permitted a large fore-and-aft travel. Later aircraft of this type were built elsewhere in the world: in England by the Bristol Company in 1952, and one year after that in the Soviet Union by fixed-wing designer Alexander S. Yakovlev, the Yak-24, a general purpose work horse (the NATO code name actually was "Horse"). Later models of the Yak-24 are still in service with the Russian Air Force. In the United States today the outstanding aircraft of this type is the Boeing-Vertol

38. *The Soviet Army transport Yak-24 has twin-tandem rotors in a configuration similar to the Boeing-Vertol V-107. Despite a general trend to turbine engines, the latest version reportedly still uses piston engines; two 1,700-horsepower Shvetsov radials. Cabin can accommodate forty troops and two 76-mm. anti-tank guns and, as photo shows, a vehicle can be carried under the fuselage when aircraft is used as a flying crane. Development of the Yak-24 began in 1952, and it was the largest production helicopter in the world until appearance of Mi-6 in 1958.*

V-107, used by the helicopter airlines, its military version, the CH-46, and a larger and more advanced design, the CH-47 Chinook.

Another effort to fly with two rotors in place of one was to return to the coaxial twin-rotor configuration used on the 1935 Bréguet helicopter. In the United States this approach was tried but then dropped by the Hiller Company in favor of the one-main-rotor one-tail-rotor design. Another new company, Bendix Helicopters, Inc., produced a successful five-place co-axial for the U.S. Navy (1947), but it was not developed further. In France, Louis Bréguet, too, experimented further with the coaxial. Ultimately, the coaxial arrangement was adopted by designer Kamov for a series of small Russian heli-copters and in the United States by the Gyrodyne Company for a small one-man helicopter that has been developed into an effective antisubmarine weapon as a remote-control drone.

Still another approach to the problem was to return to the concept of the wondrous intermesher built during the war by Anton Flettner in Germany and the Kellett Company in the United States. This "eggbeater" with its two side-by-side closely intermeshing rotors offered a good approach for a small, highly maneuverable, fast-climbing helicopter. In this configuration the two rotors are set on side-by-side masts angled outward, so the blades, as they turn, actually mesh together like the spinning mixers of an eggbeater; hence the name. In the United States, aircraft of this type were built by the Kaman Aircraft Corporation, the first having flown in January of 1947.

The important types that have been described thus far: (twin lateral rotors, the single main rotor, tandem rotor, co-axial, and synchropter) are still with us today as the primary configurations, though there have been some variations. It would be next to impossible to try to mention every worth-while new concept in helicopter design since the postwar period. Nevertheless, to bring the story up to date, in the brief-est of terms, several of the more significant developments in rotor design and propulsion systems will be discussed.

One of the most significant advances since the war has been the introduction of turbines in place of piston engines. This began on an experimental basis in the 1950's in the United States, Great Britain, and France. Constant improvement and refinement followed, with the result that piston engines are now found for the most part only in smaller or older aircraft. Performance has been so greatly improved, particularly in the heavier transport machines, that the turbine-powered helicopters—"turbocopters"—are almost a new breed of aircraft. The turbines (when used to drive a rotor shaft, they are called "turboshaft" engines) are considerably lighter, offer considerably more power than equivalent piston engines, and also permit the use of simpler rotor drive systems. The installation of a turbine power plant in a helicopter was pioneered in 1951 in the United States by Kaman with its K-225, powered by a single 190 shaft-horsepower Boeing turbine. Three years later, Kaman flew the world's first twin-turbine copter, an HTK-1 synchropter, which had its piston engine replaced by two Boeing turbines. By way of illustrating the weight and power advantage, the two turbines (total horsepower 380) weighed no more than the single 240-horsepower piston engine they replaced.

Another important innovation, stemming from the intense rotating-wing activity in Germany during the war, was the principle of using jet propulsion at the tips of the rotor blades to provide the rotating force. This, of course, eliminated the problem of torque reaction. The concept of having a tip-drive force working directly on the blades is—as with most other systems in helicopter design—an old idea; it appeared in some of the earliest unsuccessful aircraft, with propellers providing the driving force rather than jets. An aircraft of this type was the magnificently complex Curtiss-Bleecker, built in the United States in 1930, which had four huge rotors, each driven by its own full-sized propeller. Another more significant effort in this direction was the series of experimental aircraft developed between 1929 and 1935 by Vittorio Isacco, which he termed "Helicogyres"; the rotor was driven by small engines and propellers actually mounted on the blades (described in Chapter I).

German work on tip-jet propulsion dates from 1942 when

39. *Two helicopters by Soviet designer Mikhail Mil: on the right is the four-seat general-purpose Mi-1, first produced in 1951; on the left is the very large Mi-6, which first appeared in 1958, powered by two 5,500-shaft-horsepower Soloviev turbine engines. Emergence of the Mi-6, capable of carrying roughly twice the payload of the largest helicopters operational in the West at the time, served to dispel any lingering doubts about Russian progress. In September of 1963 the Mi-6 established a world's record for weight-lifting by carrying a payload of 44,350 pounds to an altitude of 2,000 meters (over 6,000 feet). Diameter of Mi-6 single main rotor is 115 feet, that of the tail rotor 21 feet.*

40. *In this 1950 photograph, tongues of flame stream from small ram-jet engines on the blade tips as test pilot Bruce James fires up the tiny Hiller Hornet. Propelling the rotor through use of small jets mounted on blade tips offers many advantages over the usual drive shaft: engine torque is eliminated, weight and mechanical complexity reduced. Unfortunately, the high fuel consumption tends to cancel out the virtues of the system. The first tip-drive helicopter actually in production, the French Sud-Aviation Djinn of 1953, did not use tip-mounted engines; instead, a flow of air from a turbine-powered compressor in the fuselage was ducted out to the tips.*

Friedrich L. Doblhoff began the development of a series of small single-rotor helicopters intended, it seems, as reconnaissance aircraft to be carried on German submarines. Within the fuselage an engine-driven compressor forced a fuel-air mixture through passages inside the hollow rotor blades to combustion chambers where the mixture was ignited and burned. Doblhoff continued to improve his system throughout the war; by 1945 four models had been built, each an improvement over previous aircraft. In the postwar period a number of designs were originated that were based on this or a similar approach. An example was the French Sud-Aviation SO-1221, the *Djinn*, which first flew in January, 1953, and later went into production. This aircraft, however, did not use flaming combustion chambers at the tips of the rotors. Instead, the engine-driven compressor in the fuselage forced plain compressed air, without any mixing of a fuel, to the blade tips, where the air ejected to the rear, thus propelling the rotor.

As a side development to the tip-drive system concept, miniature ramjet and pulse-jet engines mounted on the tips of the blades have been tested as propulsion systems for several experimental helicopters. Still another arrangement for incorporating tipdrive has been the use of small rocket motors; this has been intended primarily as a device for emergency boost power in a standard helicopter.

Another design approach in the postwar period was further experimentation with multiple-rotor aircraft, that is, helicopters with more than two main rotors. An outstanding example was the promising but ill-fated three-rotor British Cierva *Air Horse*, which made its first flight at Southampton Airport in December, 1948. Powered by a Mark 24 Rolls-Royce *Merlin* of 1,620 horsepower (the same engine used in the *Spitfire* fighter), with an all-up weight of 17,500 pounds, it was the largest transport in the world at the time. Each of its three rotors was forty-seven feet in diameter. The *Air Horse* was intended as the prototype for an even larger three-rotor aircraft, to be powered by two *Merlins*. But, tragically, in 1950 there was a disastrous crash in which key members of the

Cierva team were killed, and the three-rotor concept has not been revived since.

In the United States, a significant multiple-rotor design was the four-rotor Quadrotor flown on Long Island in 1956 by its designer and test pilot, D. H. Kaplan. The four rotors were positioned in an H configuration, and the design incorporated simplified hubs with strap-mounted blades, a form of "hingeless" rotor. Part of the appeal of multiple-rotor aircraft is that they can be designed to eliminate complex cyclic-pitch-control systems. Control in pitch and roll can be achieved with differential collective pitch between the rotors, and this system was used with marked success in the Quadrotor (a similar arrangement had also been used in the three-rotor *Air Horse*). The system was designed so that almost any combination of collective pitch changes could be introduced into the four rotors, thus varying the rotor thrust and yielding powerful control. For example, to roll the Quadrotor to one side, the pitch of both rotors on that side would be increased while the pitch of the two rotors on the other side was decreased. To achieve directional control (turning the ship to the right or left), the four rotor masts would be inclined slightly inward from the vertical, the two forward rotors tilted aft, and the two rear rotors forward. By varying the rotor thrust, forces could be produced that would yaw the aircraft around its vertical axis.

Despite successful testing and development, military support for the Quadrotor ceased after cutbacks in defense spending. However, the design—particularly its control system—was a precursor of current experimental vertical-rising aircraft designs that incorporate tandem wings or a square configuration of four fans, ducts, or jets.

Within the last ten years, a new trend in helicopter design has been toward the "compound helicopter" (another term is "convertiplane"), which offers considerable promise in raising the relatively low top speed of the standard helicopter. Interestingly, in many ways these aircraft are similar to the winged Gyroplanes flown thirty years ago. The rotor of the compound helicopter is powered for take-off; once cruising altitude is reached, the engine power is used to drive a propeller for forward thrust, and the rotor is allowed to freewheel and autorotate as do the blades of an Autogiro. The aircraft usually has small wings to furnish lift in forward flight after the rotor has been unloaded. One of the earliest compound helicopter designs was that reported as produced in Russia in 1938 by the Soviet research agency, the Central Aero-Hydrodynamic Institute. This ship, the TsAGI 11-E, had two propellers—both facing forward—which provided torque control as well as furnishing propulsion for forward flight.

In Great Britain the compound helicopter had appeared in 1947 in the form of the Fairey *Gyrodyne* designed by Dr. James A. J. Bennett. The main rotor (51 feet 8 inches in diameter) was shaft-driven, and forward thrust was secured by means of a propeller mounted off center on the right tip of the aircraft's small wing. Both the main rotor and the forward-pulling propeller were driven by the aircraft's single piston engine. This somewhat unsymmetrical arrangement worked well, and in 1948 the *Gyrodyne* established a world's speed record for helicopters of 124 miles per hour. Sadly—as with not a few experimental helicopters—this ship later crashed, killing its crew, due to a fatigue failure in the rotor hub. In 1955 a more advanced version of the *Gyrodyne* was flown with the shaft drive to the rotor elminated in favor of a tip-jet system. As with the wartime creations of Doblhoff, a compressor in the fuselage supplied the flow of air that was mixed with fuel and burned in the tip-jets. This second aircraft was used as a flying test bed in the development of Fairey's very large *Rotodyne* transport (all-up weight of 33,000 pounds), first flown in 1957. The fifty-seven passenger *Rotodyne* was powered by two Rolls-Royce turbo shaft *Tyne* engines which drove its two propellers and provided compressed air for the tip-jets as well. In 1959 the *Rotodyne* set a world's speed record, in its class, of 192 miles per hour. While in many ways a highly successful aircraft, a critical problem was the high noise level of the tip-jets, and development apparently has not been pursued further.

In the United States in the summer of 1954, the McDonnell Company flew its four-place XV-1, a compound helicopter,

41. The XV-1 developed by McDonnell Aircraft Corporation and first flown in 1954 was a compound helicopter that had features of a helicopter, airplane, and autogiro. Incorporating a tip-jet-powered rotor, wings, and a pusher propeller, the experimental XV-1 could rise vertically; after take-off the engine was shifted from supplying air from the tip-jets to driving the propeller, the wings furnished lift, and the rotor blades kept turning in autorotation. Initially the aircraft had been designated as the XH-35 by the U.S. Army and as XL-25 by the Air Force; eventually they compromised and settled on XV-1.

42. One-man helicopter with the author at the controls during flight at Westchester Airport, New York, September 1956. Design was coaxial with two sets of rotors, turning in opposite directions, below the pilot's platform. Rotor blades were fixed rigidly with no cyclic or collective pitch control. To move the aircraft, the pilot leaned in the direction he wanted to go. Control for turning was through the handle bar, which affected the rotational speed (and thus the torque) of the rotors. Manufactured by De Lackner Helicopters, Inc. it was tested by the U.S. Army during 1956 and 1957.

"convertiplane" if you prefer, powered by pressure jets at the tips of its three rotor blades.* The aircraft had a single piston engine (550-horsepower Continental) which supplied air to the tip-jet burners during vertical flight and then turned a pusher propeller, located behind the cabin, for thrust in forward flight. This location for the propeller was made possible by the XV-1's unique configuration: its tail surfaces were supported by twin booms running back from the wing, on each side of the fuselage nacelle. Successful inflight conversions from helicopter to airplane regime were made and eventually the XV-1 was flown at what was then a phenomenally high speed for rotating wing aircraft, approximately 200 miles per hour.

Although much larger and somewhat faster, the Kamov Ka-22 which attracted world attention at the Soviet Aviation Day Tushino air display in 1961 could be considered as the Russian counterpart to the *Rotodyne*. This remarkable compound helicopter, named the *Vintokrulya* ("screw wing"), has two four-bladed rotors—each about the size of the rotor of the Mi-4 helicopter—mounted side by side at the tips of a 90-foot wing, in the manner of the earlier Bratukhin *Omegas* and the wartime Focke aircraft. Two Ivchenko turboshaft engines, mounted at each wing tip, turn the two conventional propellers for forward propulsion as well as directly driving the two main rotors. Capable of carrying over 80 passengers, the Vintokrulya has exhibited good maneuverability, hovering characteristics, and, since there are no tip-jets, fairly low noise levels as well—of particular importance if the aircraft is used for feeder airline operations in densely populated areas. After the 1961 display the Ka-22 described as the world's most powerful vertical take-off aircraft, went on to set no less than seven Fédération Aeronautique Internationale records, including a top speed of 221.39 miles per hour and a notable payload-to-altitude performance of 36,343 pounds lifted to a height of 6,562 feet.

The intense activity that has gone into the refinement and improvement of rotating-wing aircraft in the last decade has

* Friedrich L. Doblhoff was helicopter chief engineer at McDonnell during the XV-1 Program.

helped to create a new "family" of aircraft, which hover under the term "V/STOL's." The capital letters stand for "Vertical/Short Take-Off and Landing" aircraft.* It is not intended here to attempt a description of each of the many V/STOL's; almost every imaginable combination of rotors, wings, propellers, and jet engines has been tried as designers once again have been involved with aircraft that have never before been seen on the face of the earth. It is perhaps more useful to consider the reasons for the development of the V/STOL's.

The V/STOL breed has resulted from the search for ways to increase the helicopter's speed and range so that it might begin to compete with the airplane while retaining the ability to take off vertically. The problem, as always, is the rotor; you need it to pull the machine straight up, but once in forward flight the drag of the rotor, and control problems, prevent any reasonable speed. Experimenters have been steadily re-designing rotor systems to make them more suitable for high forward speed. (The current goal is between 200 and 250 miles per hour, not just for a specially souped-up and modified speed ship but for the standard production helicopter. The increase in speed is perhaps wanted most for the heavy transport types.) One important concept is Lockheed's "rigid rotor" which incorporates a hub that permits the blades only one freedom, that of changing pitch. An experimental rigid-rotor aircraft built by Lockheed for the Army, the XH-1A, equipped with a small wing and jet engine for added forward thrust—a form of compound helicopter—has been reported as flying as fast as 272 miles per hour in tests, a phenomenal speed for a rotorcraft.

In some cases the designer has tried to do away with the rotor entirely. Instead, he may use oversize propellers that can tilt either straight up for vertical take-off or directly forward to pull the ship through the air. In many of these systems, the wings tilt along with the propeller shafts; not surprisingly these aircraft are called *tilt-props* or *tilt-wings*.

In very broad terms, this introduction to the compound helicopter and the other V/STOL's serves to bring the story up to date, at least from the technical viewpoint. In retrospect,

* These new types are discussed more fully in Chapter VI.

there seem to have been two dissimilar trends at work. One has been the constant struggle to refine and improve the basic helicopter configurations which were developed, for the most part, during World War II or in the postwar period. The other trend, if it can be called that, has been to pass from the realm of the true helicopter to more exotic types such as the V/STOL's.

Obviously, there is a great deal more to the story of the helicopter than the historical and technical details. Rotating-wing aircraft have had their effect on the world we live; to get anything like a true picture, the various uses—such as military operations, air rescue, and transportation—have to be examined. Separate chapters in this book cover many of these areas; nevertheless, a quick review here will be helpful to put the technical developments into the proper perspective.

During World War II the newly-developed helicopter saw only limited use, primarily for patrol and rescue service. With the advent of the Korean War, its role was gradually enlarged to include out-and-out use as a weapon of war—for transport of men and supplies, for armed reconnaissance, and for combatting guerrilla forces in inaccessible areas. The newest term for this is "counter-insurgency," or, in Pentagonese, COIN operations. The United States commitment in Vietnam, particularly, has seen the rise of the armed helicopter, the gunship, intended as a weapons platform capable of closing with the enemy on the ground. Inexorably, the development of any type of aircraft has always been linked with its role in war, and the helicopter is no exception.

But in the postwar period, despite the high cost of operations, the helicopter has become increasingly a general-purpose vehicle for an endless number of civilian jobs as well, including all sorts of charter operations and specialized work: crop dusting, power line inspection, prospecting for minerals (the helicopter has practically replaced the faithful mule as the stereotyped companion of the bewhiskered prospector), almost every kind of patrol activity—especially for the police, and the observation and reporting of highway traffic conditions, to mention a few such uses.

Some measure of the helicopter's popularity lies in its use by national political figures. So often are candidates for election aloft as they roam the landscape after votes, that the traditional whistle-stop visit by train has given way to the "helistop" handshake. The industry feels that the general all-around use of helicopters for specialized jobs and for nonscheduled transportation service (charter work and what might be called "helicab" service) will continue to increase steadily. This optimism may be well founded, though critics point to various developments that are necessary before growth can occur: a reduction in the cost of owning and operating helicopters, an improvement in the ability to fly in bad weather, and third, and perhaps most important, the increased availability of places for helicopters to land in key areas—in other words, more heliports and helipads.

At the same time that the use of helicopters in these specialized jobs has increased,* so has the appeal of the helicopter for true airline service in regularly scheduled flights. The first scheduled air-mail flight by helicopter was made on October 1, 1947, by Los Angeles Airways, helicopter operator in that area, and in the early 1950's passenger "copterline" service was begun in three major American cities—New York, Chicago, and Los Angeles—and by two regular airlines in Europe. The Russians, with cities located vast distances apart and served by only rudimentary ground transportation systems, also began important city helicopter service during this period.

Besides the military operations, the helicopter airlines, the charter operators, and all the various specialized jobs, there is still another potential use that has tantalized the industry for years. This is the fond hope that eventually small two-place helicopters will be sufficiently inexpensive and easy to fly, that they can be bought and flown by many prosperous Americans. The comparison has often been made to sports cars: the idea

* In the United States, in 1960, there were 936 civilian helicopters in service, and by mid-1965 this had risen to 2,053. In 1960 the number of civilian operators totaled 318; by mid-1965 this had climbed to 860.

is that a small, simple helicopter would appeal to the kind of people — young, alert, devil-may-care, and well-to-do — who ordinarily buy these expensive ground vehicles. The thought remains a fantasy—the least expensive two-place helicopter in production costs approximately $24,000, which is considerably more than the price of a sports car. By way of comparison, however, about ten years ago the least expensive small helicopter cost approximately $50,000 and there have been continued efforts to produce a practical low-cost helicopter.

IV

A Rope of Rescue

"We want people to know that it's not just a stunt. It really
works. Just imagine what we could do with a couple hundred
of them. . . ."
      —COL. PHILIP D. COCHRAN, U.S. Army Air Force (1944)

"Then a helicopter approaches braving the gale,
  A rope of rescue down swaying by the wind,
Cling to a life raft for their lives,
  Thus fourteen Japanese seamen were saved,
Ah, calm and heroic Lieutenant Gates."
      —From a poem by KIKUJU KOMORI, Tokyo (1955)

IGOR I. SIKORSKY has an anonymous brochure in his possession,
published in Paris in 1862, entitled *L'Aeronef, appareil de
sauvetage (Aircraft, Device for Saving Lives)*. In it the writer
describes his vision of a helicopter and then argues for the construction of such a machine. The unknown author clearly pre-
dicts the use of the aircraft for rescue, ending with the statement: "And then I, a modest narrator . . . will have the
happiness to see people rescued at sea, and the victims of fire
and flood saved by this apparatus."
  Although this piece of early pro-helicopter propaganda is
unsigned, the circumstantial evidence points to the indefatiga-
ble Viscomte Ponton d'Amecourt or, perhaps, to one of his
associates. Whoever the writer, his prophecy and his wish have

been borne out in reality to an extent that, surely, he could never have imagined. Since World War II, when the first operational helicopters went into service, the aircraft have been used constantly for rescue and lifesaving missions in every corner of the world. In 1964, Sikorsky guessed that his helicopters alone had saved at least fifty thousand lives and that the total for the industry was probably over a hundred thousand.

It is difficult to pin down the very first lifesaving mission flown by a helicopter. One of the first to receive public attention in the United States was an operation during World War II by a Sikorsky YR-4 assigned to the Coast Guard, near New York City, on January 3, 1944. However, other YR-4's were in service with American forces at the time, and it is possible that a similar—though unrecorded—mission might have been flown earlier. Another consideration is that there were operational helicopters flying in other countries during this period. The Germans, in particular, had the highly advanced Flettner Fl-282 in production (by late 1943 twenty had been built) and in service with their navy; it may well have been used for such missions.

The YR-4 flown by the Coast Guard pilot was a direct descendant of Sikorsky's first helicopter, the experimental VS-300 described in Chapter III, which had made its first short hop—tethered to the ground with cables—on September 14, 1939. The experience gained from the development of the VS-300 had been translated into the design of the larger XR-4 ("X" for experimental, "R" for rotating wing, "4" for the fourth Army helicopter contract). After successful trials, the "X" was dropped and the aircraft became the YR-4—the "Y" indicating a limited-production status.

Though only a short overwater hop of 15 miles, the flight of the Coast Guard helicopter during the freezing rain and snow of that January day was no publicity stunt. A powerful explosion had ripped through a Navy destroyer off the New Jersey coast, killing many of the crew, burning and maiming others. The seventy injured men were sent ashore to a hospital at

43. *An Air Force H-19 of the 33rd Air Rescue Squadron hoists a crewman from the Army tug LT-578 after she foundered on a reef less than a mile off the Okinawa coast. All twenty-eight crew members were saved after pounding surf forced open the tug's watertight doors. The helicopter is the military version of the Sikorsky S-55 used by Army and Air Force in the Korean War. Power plant is a 600-horsepower Pratt and Whitney piston engine; maximum speed, approximately 95 miles per hour; range, 350 miles.*

Sandy Hook, where they were cared for on the spot. The pressing need was for blood plasma, lots of it and fast, especially for the burn cases. Plasma was available in Manhattan, only 15 miles across the bay, but the weather was bad: snow, rain, freezing winds. A boat would take over an hour, a trip by car even longer.

Navy officials remembered the few YR-4's then stationed at the Floyd Bennett Field Coast Guard base in Brooklyn. The request was made, and Commander Frank A. Erickson, one of the few qualified helicopter pilots, had a boxy, fabric-covered YR-4 rolled out and warmed up. Through snow squalls, sleet, and high winds, he flew straight to the Battery at the tip of Manhattan, where two cases of blood plasma were waiting. They were loaded aboard, and the YR-4 went bumping across the bay, buffeted by gusts. Fourteen minutes later, its wheels settled gently on the beach at Sandy Hook, and forty units of plasma were rushed to the survivors. Mission accomplished, Commander Erickson promptly eased his aircraft back into the air and in another fifteen minutes was back at the Floyd Bennett base.

This short overwater flight does not seem a particularly awe-inspiring feat, even in bad weather. But it should be appreciated that the YR-4's engine, a seven-cylinder Warner *Scarab* of some 180 horsepower, was mounted on its side although it had initially been designed to run upright in an airplane. Occasionally, the *Scarab* complained about this unreasonable situation, and its complaints had the habit of appearing during overwater flights. Still, the flight was uneventful. It demonstrated that a helicopter could be expected, as a matter of routine, to save human lives.

The mercy mission flown by Commander Erickson attracted considerable public attention to the newly developed helicopter. The incident was widely reported, and newspapers commented favorably upon it. The *New York Times* devoted editorial space to praising the flight and sensibly predicted that the copter would be widely used in lifesaving and rescue work.

During the year that followed, different branches of the armed forces engaged in further experiments, including various air rescue trials. These tests provided more evidence on the value of the new aircraft. Underpowered, it vibrated and shook and was by no means perfected, but everyone agreed that it worked. World War II was raging, the helicopter might save the lives of Americans in combat, provided it got there in time, and preparations were made to send the YR-4's overseas.

The earliest combat rescue operation by a United States helicopter seems to have taken place during the latter part of April, 1944, in the Far East. The area was the jungle of north central Burma, then a battleground between the Allies and the Japanese. A considerable number of light planes, approximately one hundred, attached to the India-based First Air Commando Group, were being used in support of the British "Chindits," a far-ranging penetration force operating behind the enemy lines. This light-plane operation—one of the first in history of such size—turned in a remarkable performance in a general liaison role, especially in flying in supplies and evacuating the wounded. According to a contemporary U.S. Army report, "estimates of combat sorties flown vary from 5,000 to 8,000 . . . the number of casualties flown is believed to exceed 2,000."

Four YR-4 helicopters were included in the Air Commando array of aircraft, but none was involved in operations until late in April, when one of the light planes (an L-1) was forced down by engine failure not far behind the Japanese lines. Three British soldiers were aboard, besides the pilot (two wounded, the third a malaria case) and all survived the crash. There was no cleared area available in which to land a rescue plane, so the stage was set for use of one of the helicopters. The Army report* on the operation devoted five paragraphs to the rescue, which it called ". . . the first use of the helicopter in evacuation —certainly behind enemy lines." The incident, a historic first for the U.S. Army Air Force, was described in the report as follows:

> Notes were dropped to the light plane pilot (by another light plane) directing him to take his passengers up a ridge, away from

* Report 3137, dated 30 May 1944, from JICA/CBI, New Delhi, India.

Japanese in the vicinity. Two of the passengers had gunshot wounds, in arm and shoulder, and the third was a malaria case. The party made its way up the ridge, nevertheless, and lived these four nights with supplies of food and water dropped by light planes.

Meantime, a YR-4 (two-place) helicopter piloted by 1st Lt. Carter Harman took off at Lalaghat 21 April and flew by stages to Hailakandi, Khumbirgram, Dimapur and Jorhat, crossing the 6000 foot range en route. The next day, the helicopter flew to Ledo and Taro, where an extra tank was installed for the long fly-in to "Aberdeen". The helicopter arrived at "Aberdeen" the afternoon of 23 April, crossing the ranges from Ledo successfully, and immediately was sent on its first mission.

The stranded party of four men was told by dropped note to descend to a small paddy field, about 25 miles south of "Aberdeen". The helicopter was flown to a light plane strip about 5 miles away from the paddy clearing and there received a wig-wag signal from a light plane that the party was ready to be rescued. Lt. Harman made two flights to the paddy clearing, returning each time one of the two wounded men to the light plane strip, where they were transferred to a light plane and taken to "Aberdeen". Then the helicopter became inoperable because of excessive heat and had to be left on the advance strip overnight. The following day, the helicopter rescued the remaining two men—the light plane pilot last.

On 24 April the helicopter was returned to "Aberdeen" and thereafter until 4 May flew 4 more "jobs", including the pickup of 2 more casualties—one of whom had to be strapped in. In all, a total of 23 combat sorties were flown from Ledo. Chief difficulty was found to be a propensity of the YR-4 to overheat, causing motor failure.

On 4 May the helicopter was ordered away from "Aberdeen" when a Japanese bombing attack destroyed or damaged all planes on the field except the helicopter. Lt. Harman flew it back to Lalaghat in five troublesome days. Encountering thunderstorms in the mountains on the Dimapur-Khumbirgram leg, he made two landings in valley clearings, at 1500 and 2000 feet—believed to be the highest recorded landings for a helicopter—and awaited a change in the weather.

The term "Aberdeen," used repeatedly in the report, was the code name for a strong point held by the Chindits that was actually located behind the enemy lines. This tactic was perfected by their brilliant and unorthodox commander, Brigadier General Orde Wingate. It called for holding carefully chosen positions in enemy territory (in Wingate's own language each was a "stronghold") that could be easily defended and offered sufficient clear space for an airstrip. Wingate, who evolved long-range penetration tactics for raids deep in enemy areas, had fought and defeated Axis forces in Palestine, Ethiopia, and then Burma. Wingate had been killed before the time of the helicopter rescue, in March, 1944, in the crash of an American medium bomber, a B-25 Mitchell. The Aberdeen stronghold was evacuated and closed down early in May, shortly after the mission of the YR-4 had been completed.

Despite the success of this first rescue mission, there was still some question about the usefulness of the YR-4, which had showed various imperfections; it was underpowered and the engine tended to overheat, as well. But Colonel Philip D. Cochran, commander of the First Air Commando group, had witnessed the rescue at Aberdeen and was not one of the doubters. He put it in straightforward language at the time: "We want people to know that it's not just a stunt. It really works. Just imagine what we could do with a couple hundred of them. . . ."

Twenty-two years later, in March of 1966, former Air Force Colonel Cochran had occasion to remember this rescue operation during a luncheon in Stratford, Connecticut, honoring Igor I. Sikorsky. It was recalled that Carter Harman had been awarded the Distinguished Flying Cross, and Phil Cochran described the maneuvering that had been necessary to get the four very scarce helicopters assigned to his First Air Commando:

> Well, we started to form the First Air Commando Group. We collected P-51s, B-25s, gliders, DC-3s, L-5s, and organized a sizable task force. We got the men we wanted from other theaters. We had three squadrons of L-5s set to operate behind the lines, and we began to look at helicopters. . . .
>
> We were feeling a little heady right then. General Arnold said: "I've got you everything you want, haven't I?" I said: "No, sir.

We'd like some helicopters." Well, helicopters were hard to get. Sikorsky was building R-4s, but they were going to the Navy and the Coast Guard and the British. None for the Air Force. Well, Johnny Alison* had been in Russia on a liaison mission, and he'd gotten to know presidential advisor Harry Hopkins there. Alison talked to Hopkins. Project 9 (that was the code name for our Burma mission) got four YR-4Bs. General Arnold's parting words were: "How did you ever get those helicopters?"

We felt responsibility not to use the YR-4Bs as some sort of a stunt. And we didn't. Our reports showed the YR-4Bs that escaped damage in shipment and in crackups saved 18 lives. I remember a YR-4B went out to pick up two boys, both wounded, from a clearing 3,000 feet up. There were Japanese troops on the road below. There was one litter attached to the helicopter, and the weight of both men at that altitude and in that spot was a problem. Carter Harman said: "Well, let's take a crack at it." One boy got on the litter, another clung to the side of the helicopter. He got both out.

Eventually the Sikorsky YR-4 was improved; its engine was replaced with a more powerful 200-horsepower version, the "Y" was dropped, and the aircraft became the R-4, a fully accepted production model for the Army Air Force. Meanwhile, in April, 1945, during the last days of the war, one of the "Y" models was used for another rescue in the Burma jungle.

This episode began with the flight of a small, single-engine PT-19 airplane on a search mission for the crew of a downed transport plane. The region was the Naga Hills of northern Burma, less than 50 miles from Assam and roughly 200 miles from the border of mountainous Tibet. With the pilot, Captain James L. Green, was a chief of the local Naga tribe, flying as a guide. After hours of fruitless search, Green turned back to his field at Shingbwiyang, a major Allied base on the Ledo Road. But, with only a few miles to go, the PT-19's engine began to cough and sputter. It finally quit and, too low to jump, Captain Green and the Naga tribesman rode the little monoplane down.

The last thing Captain Green remembered was the crumpling of the wings as they slammed through the trees. Badly injured

---

* As a military unit, the First Air Commando was unique in many ways. Not the least of these was the fact that it had two joint commanding officers of equal rank, Colonel Cochran and Colonel John Alison.

and knocked unconscious by the crash, Green's luck was bad. But the luck of the helpful native chief was worse: he was killed outright.

Before going in, Green had managed a last-minute radio call to the airfield at Shingbwiyang. Army pilots promptly got into the air, and within a few hours they had located the scene of the crash. Bringing in help, however, was a problem not so easily solved. The crash was actually only three minutes' flying time from the airfield; Green had been almost in the airfield's pattern when he crashed. But the terrain was so bad that rescue and medical parties had to work their way over tortuous mountain trails for more than a day before they could get to the smashed wreckage. Medics examined Green, gave him an injection to ease his pain, and then began to worry about how to get him out. The pilot was in such bad shape that the idea of carrying him up and down those ridges was out of the question; it would probably have killed him.

A new YR-4 helicopter was available at the Shingbwiyang base; it had been flown in from the states a few months before to aid in another search but had arrived too late. It didn't take long for the rescue party to decide that it was the only way to get Green out alive. The next problem was to clear a flat, open area for the helicopter to land on. It was no small job; many of the trees were well over 100 feet high. A detachment of Army Combat Engineers were requested, then a volunteer group from the air crews of the 2nd Troop Carrier Squadron, Tenth Air Force, stationed at the airfield, came in to help. Equipment, medical supplies, and food were parachuted in for almost two weeks while a level area was carved and blasted from the jungle.

On April 4, more than two weeks after the PT-19 had crashed on March 21, The YR-4 touched down at the jungle clearing and flew Green to the front door of the hospital at Shingbwiyang. The actual rescue went off well enough except for a few bad moments right after take-off when, according to a report made by the Tenth Air Force, there was a loss in engine power. "As a result the helicopter lost between 10 and 15 feet in altitude almost immediately following movement beyond the

44. *The Army's YR-4 Sikorsky helicopter was used in the rescue of Captain James L. Green from the jungle near Shingbwiyang, Burma, in April of 1945. The first United States helicopter to see active military service, the YR-4 was built along light-plane lines: the fuselage and the rotor blades were fabric-covered. Invaluable though they were for rescue operations, the YR-4's were underpowered; the engine was a 180-horsepower Warner, later upped to 200 horsepower. The engine compartment, located directly behind the pilot, had transparent plastic covers.*

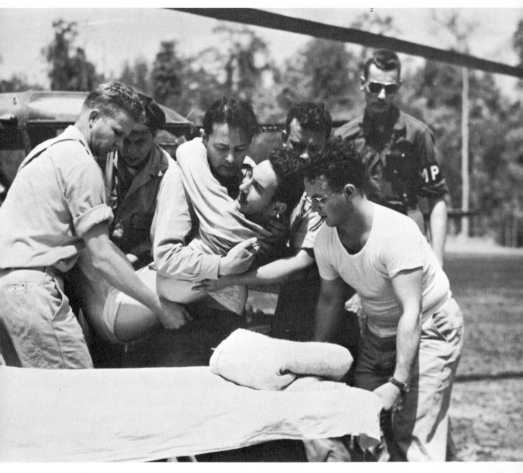

45. *Captain Green is lifted gently from the YR-4 after flight from the scene of his airplane crash. As he was badly injured and delirious when found, it was impossible to carry him out through the jungle, so a small clearing was made on a ledge near the crash and the YR-4 flown in from its base at Myitkyina. Helicopter had to make three passes before it could land safely in the clearing. "Like landing in a well," was the comment of pilot Lieutenant Raymond F. Murdock.*

ledge of the clearing. Fortunately the edge of the clearing was
sharply defined. . . . This afforded a space area which absorbed
the drop in altitude." The report summed up the incident by
noting the YR-4's deficiency in power at altitudes above sea
level and pointed out that the rescue had been made at a
height of 1,200 feet. It also suggested, respectfully, that helicopters of "greater horsepower and altitude potentialities" be
obtained.

As the war ended, more R-4's were being sent overseas,
eventually to be replaced by newer ships that were already in
production. But with the end of hostilities there were fewer
opportunities to use helicopters in lifesaving missions. Nevertheless, at peacetime bases scattered in remote areas around
the world and in the continental United States, there were
important incidents, each a kind of minor miracle in lifesaving.
The art of copter rescue continued to advance, but not at the
pace experienced during the war.

One of the first rescues of the peacetime era, and probably
the first at sea from a sinking vessel, occurred on November 29,
1945, in Long Island Sound, New York, not far from the
Sikorsky home plant at Bridgeport, Connecticut. On the previous day, after a towline had parted during a howling north-
east gale, an oil barge had gone aground on Penfield Reef, off
Fairfield Connecticut. Two men were marooned aboard, and
rescue by surface craft had been impossible because of the
high winds and raging seas. The next day the storm continued
unabated, and the barge began to show signs of breaking up
as it pounded on the reef.

After the men had spent sixteen hours aboard, an Army
R-5* flown directly from the Bridgeport plant managed to get
through, despite 30- to 60-mile-per-hour winds and driving
rain. Dimitry D. "Jimmy" Viner, chief Sikorsky pilot, and
nephew of Igor I. Sikorsky, was at the controls, while Army
Captain Jackson E. Beighle manned the rescue hoist, a new

* The R-5 was later redesigned and modified to become the widely-used
civilian S-51. During the Korean War the S-51, used by the Air Force, was given
the military designation of H-5.

46. *One of the first peacetime rescues, November 29, 1945: an Army R-5 flown directly from the Sikorsky plant at Bridgeport, Connecticut, by chief test pilot Dimitry D. Viner, hovers over a barge wrecked on Penfield Reef to pull up the two survivors with its then-new rescue hoist.*

feature on helicopters. Two trips were made during the rescue; the first man was winched up into the cabin for the trip ashore, but on the second mission the winch jammed and Viner had to fly back with the seaman still dangling from the hoist cable. The ability of the R-5 to hover over the stricken barge, in spite of the gale-force wind, demonstrated the controllability of a helicopter, even during turbulence and foul weather.

More peacetime incidents followed. Not many were as dramatic as the in-the-nick-of-time mission over Penfield Reef, but each served to illustrate the inherent ability of the helicopter as a rescue vehicle. Helicopters saved fliers trapped in Canadian snowdrifts after a plane crash, rescued men trapped on floating ice in Lake Erie, took food to the stranded passengers of a snowbound train, and rushed medical aid to accident scenes.

During these few years of peace before the Korean War, the U.S. Navy began using helicopters regularly for standby rescue, during take-off and landing of airplanes operating with aircraft carriers. One of the first incidents was the snatching of Lieutenant Frank A. Shields from the ocean on February 9, 1947, after he had ditched his Curtiss SB2C dive bomber near the aircraft carrier U.S.S. *Leyte*. A Sikorsky HO3S-1 helicopter (the same aircraft as the Air Force H-5) that was being tested with the 2nd Task Force Atlantic Fleet picked up Shields and deposited him safely back aboard the *Leyte* in just six minutes.

Despite these advances, it was not until the Korean War that a turning point was reached in the development of the helicopter, as a rescue vehicle and for general military use as well. Tested in World War II and improved in the few years of peace that followed, it had become reasonably efficient and reliable. The bitter struggle in Korea would result in more improvements and demonstrate dramatically the lifesaving abilities of the machine, particularly in that fateful first year when United Nations forces were often isolated and surrounded.

One of the earliest—if not the earliest—helicopter rescue

47. *Two American-made helicopters were used to evacuate French soldiers wounded in the conflict in Vietnam (then called Indo-China) as early as 1949, before the beginning of the Korean War. These aircraft were small Hiller Model 360's equipped with medical evacuation litters attached to the side of the fuselage. Here, casualties are evacuated from a bloody action near Thai Binh. One of the pilots in the unit was a woman, Mlle. Valerie André, a French Army surgeon who flew her own aerial ambulance.*

operations in Korea took place on August 4, 1950, about a month after the start of the war.* A Marine Corps Sikorsky HO3S-1 began the evacuation of casualties during a battle near a town called Chindongni. The copters belonged to an observation squadron, VMO-6, and they were not equipped with litters or other provisions for handling the wounded. Battlefield modifications were made: the right window was removed entirely, and fittings were installed to hold a stretcher. It worked well, even though the patient's feet stuck out a foot and a half through the window.

The work horse of the Marine and Air Force rescue operations during the first year of the Korean War was the Sikorsky H-5. It had more than twice the power of the R-4's of World War II and could carry a pilot and a medic, as well as two patients in pods mounted on the fuselage. Though slow and unarmored, as were all helicopters of that era, the H-5's were not easy to shoot down. It was demonstrated again and again that, surprisingly, the rotors were not especially vulnerable. Provided the main spar of the blade was not touched, they could take hits and the ship would keep right on flying.

The first true helicopter air rescue group in Korea was the unit activated by the Air Force at Taegu, late in September of 1950, roughly three months after the war had begun. A detachment of the Third Air Rescue Squadron, the unit was equipped with a handful of H-5 helicopters as well as a number of small fabric-covered Stinson L-5 airplanes. The unit had just eleven officers and fifty-six enlisted men to accomplish the job at hand. Despite primitive facilities and limited equipment, by the end of the year—the first six months of the war—the helicopters had transported 618 medical cases. The smaller L-5 airplanes had flown 56 cases.

The beginning of 1951 saw bitter fighting in freezing winter weather, as United Nations forces battled a second big invasion from the north. The first had been the North Korean Army; after it had been defeated, the Chinese swept down the peninsula. On February 15, the Air Rescue detachment at

* The invasion from North Korea began before dawn, Sunday morning, June 25, 1950.

48. *A tableau of the Korean War, December, 1951: medical corps-men carry a wounded soldier to a helicopter for evacuation to a rear-line hospital, watched by the grim-faced pilot. This scene was repeated thousands of times before signing of the truce ended the conflict, emphasizing the value of helicopters for this work. The aircraft is an Air Force Sikorsky H-5 (civilian designation S-51). Initially manufactured and flown in 1946, it was the first helicopter used in Korea and saw extensive service as a "last-chance taxi."*

Taegu was called upon for what was considered a dangerous and difficult mission for helicopters. American troops, trapped in a pocket some twenty miles east of the Korean capital city of Seoul, were surrounded and literally fighting for their lives, with many wounded. They needed everything—ammunition, food, blankets—but medical aid was the top-priority item. Loaded with blood plasma and other carefully chosen medical supplies, six Sikorsky H-5's (every available one at Taegu) went out that afternoon and began a regular shuttle run between the home base and the beseiged men. The six Sikorskys kept the shuttle operation going until the blackness of the Korean winter night closed in. Each managed to fly three missions into the pocket with the needed supplies; on the way back they took out the worst of the wounded infantrymen, a total of thirty.

At the first glimmer of daylight the next morning at Taegu, the ground crews were out on the iron-hard frozen earth of the airstrip, warming up and checking the H-5's for another round of action. As their preflight inspections progressed they found that two of the six aircraft had to be grounded. The remaining four flew out as soon as there was enough light to see the frozen rice paddies stretching to the northwest in the direction of Seoul. The weather was poor: low cloud and snow. Later in the day it got worse, the snow increased, and the wind rose to over 40 miles an hour. The top speed of the H-5, even a fast one, was rarely over 80 miles per hour, and the wind interfered considerably. Nevertheless, by the end of the second day twenty-two more badly wounded soldiers were flown out, raising the total for both days to fifty-two.

By now active support from United Nations fighter aircraft, bombing and strafing the encircling Chinese, was having its effect. Air Force C-119 *Flying Boxcar* transport planes were dropping heavy supplies, including belts of .30- and .50-caliber machine-gun ammunition. Bolstered by this heavy support from the air, the beseiged men were able to break out of the trap.

The next major action of this detachment was not a response to a message for help but an operation that had been carefully planned beforehand. It involved the evacuation of more than

300 wounded and injured paratroopers after a mass jump on March 23, 1951, in an area north of Seoul and just south of the much-fought-over 38th Parallel. (This second-largest drop of the Korean War had caught the Chinese by surprise; it helped to consolidate United Nation gains during the drive to push the enemy back north.)

Seven H-5's were assigned to the mission of evacuating the wounded and the jump casualties. Fifteen minutes after the 187th Regimental Combat Team had completed their parachute drop into the area, the helicopters were at work in the drop zone. Enemy ground fire was heavy, and two H-5's were hit by small-arms fire on their first trip into the combat zone. The damage was minor, and the two ships kept flying.

The first H-5 to land in a rice paddy next to the scattered parachutes of the 187th troopers was flown by Captain Harry Copsey of Estes Park, Colorado. He expected some small-arms fire, but surprisingly the Chinese opened up with mortars as well. Remembering the intensity of their fire, he said later that "despite all efforts . . . they continued sniping at us all day whenever we came in for another load." The parachute troops had jumped into an area some 18 miles from the nearest friendly force, and the Chinese were determined that a link-up would not be made.

From the morning of the drop, on March 23, through the next six days, the seven H-5's flew a total of 147 sorties into the rifle and machine-gun fire and mortar blasts ringing the zone. On March 29, the last pickup of wounded was made; other United Nations forces had finally managed to break through to the paratroopers.

Often during this operation helicopter pickups were made in areas that were accessible to ground vehcles, but the H-5's were used anyway because they were so much faster. The smoothness of copter flight for moving the wounded was also beginning to be appreciated. It spared them the terrible jouncing along the rough roads.

Besides the Air Force and Marine Corps Sikorskys, a third force of helicopters was now flying organized rescue missions along the battle front: those of the U.S. Army. These aircraft were versatile Bell H-13's, small two-seaters comparable in size to the light planes used by the Army for spotting artillery fire and for liaison.* A wounded man carried in an H-13 sat in the cockpit directly alongside the pilot, just as in the old R-4's.

For one of the first battlefield evacuations by Army helicopters we have to go back to early January of 1951, when the tides of battle were just beginning to turn in favor of the United Nations. This mission was flown in an H-13 by Captain Albert C. Seburn, Commander of the 2nd Army Helicopter Detachment operating at Seoul. The detachment had just four pilots and four helicopters, yet by January 14 they had accomplished so much that all four men were awarded the Distinguished Flying Cross. One mission flown by all four H-13's involved the evacuation of twenty-three badly wounded men from a surrounded battalion. On the return trips they flew in some ten thousand rounds of ammunition. The measure of their effort is indicated by the fact that with only its four small ships the detachment brought out more than five hundred wounded men in the month of January.

An example of an Army mission in April of the same year was the evacuation in one of the small H-13's of critically wounded Lieutenant John Hodges, son of Major General Hodges, Deputy Commander of the 8th Army. The flight probably saved his life; because of the severity of his wounds it was unlikely he would have survived the trip over the rugged Korean hills in a jeep.

The speed of helicopter rescue for the wounded plus the elimination of the inevitable rough handling when moved by vehicle on the ground, saved many United Nations soldiers. This, added to the prompt medical attention, made possible a heavy drop in the death rate—the Army reported that it was cut to less than half that of World War II. It was estimated that, all told, at least fifteen thousand men were evacuated by helicopter, and the lives of three thousand seriously injured men were saved by being moved within twenty minutes after being wounded.

---

* In January of 1951 the Army began to receive another type of helicopter as well, the two-place Hiller H-23.

Eventually, as the Korean struggle escalated and more men and equipment were committed, every branch of the armed forces had reason to appreciate the value of the helicopter. Its development had actually followed the same pattern as that of the airplane: initially for observation, then transportation and rescue (airplanes were used as flying ambulances even as long ago as the Kaiser's war), and, finally, as out-and-out weapons. But, it was the rescue missions that caught the imagination of the world and dramatized what the helicopter could do. It became a "last-chance taxi" to men who otherwise might have died without the medical help they needed.

As the first year of the Korean War drew to a close, the rescue missions were bringing helicopters and their crews more frequently into contact with enemy fire. This happened often when the aircraft were used to pick up United Nations pilots who had been shot down just inside enemy lines. Inevitably, the crews began to fire back with small arms; carbines, rifles, automatic weapons. One of the first incidents, involving the rescue of a Marine fighter pilot by an Air Force H-5, occurred in June 1951, almost a year after the war had started.

This foreshadowed a new role for the helicopter—as a true weapon of war. During the last stages of World War II and throughout this first year in Korea, its role, for the most part, had been that of a merciful noncombatant, fulfilling the idealistic dreams of the visionaries and pioneers; the aircraft used had been modified civilian types that had performed surprisingly well. This time was almost over; new military types were on the way—big, fast troop carriers and armed gunships equipped with batteries of machine guns and rockets.

The helicopter's adolescence as a rescue vehicle was short, but it spanned two wars. In the years that followed, the aircraft were used increasingly in civilian rescue operations and began to affect the lives of people everywhere. An early operation that pioneered the use of helicopters in a new field—public health—occurred in the Fall of 1951 in Costa Rica.

During the summer, an epidemic of yellow fever had broken out in the interior of this small Central American country.

Mustering his limited medical resources, Dr. Oscar Vargas, the Director of Health, attempted to halt the fever. But during the heat of the summer months, it spread inexorably, even appearing beyond the borders of Costa Rica in neighboring Nicaragua and Panama. The inhabitants of the region were spread out in many small, isolated villages, settlements, and farms. When a request for medical aid was forwarded through the U.S. State Department, it was realized that a helicopter would offer an ideal means of moving a medical team throughout the area. As the program got underway, an Air Force Sikorsky H-5 was loaded aboard a big C-82 transport plane at March Air Force Base in California and flown to Costa Rica by members of Flight "B" of the 4th Air Rescue Squadron. The helicopter arrived on September 11.

Piloted by 1st Lieutenant John R. Peacock, the copter went into operation from an advanced base established at the town of Altamira near the Nicaraguan border, flying medical personnel and material into the affected areas. During an eleven-day period, forty-two landings were made throughout an area covering more than 6,000 square miles. An important part of the job was coping with the lack of communications: many missions were flown simply to alert the population and request that they assemble for inoculation. A total of 978 people in all were inoculated. Five months after it had begun, the epidemic was finally checked.

By the standards of today, the Costa Rican mission was a small operation. Yet, it was significant, for it served to show the way. One helicopter alone, in a short time, had accomplished what many ground teams had been unable to do. An epidemic that might have raged unchecked had been stopped in its tracks, largely because of the ability of an airborne team to blanket a remote area with needed medical service.

An important side-effect of the operation in Central America was the friendly feeling generated for the United States. And, if the hard-working medical team in Costa Rica accomplished this quietly and undramatically, an incident occurred in Japan during the winter of 1955 that was quite the reverse. An epic tale of rescue at sea if there ever was one, it created much good will and gratitude among the seafaring Japanese.

A small single-stack coastal freighter named the *Tanda Maru* had been driven aground on a reef off the Japanese coast. Lying low in the water and actually broken in two by mountainous waves, the ship was doomed. Clinging to the rigging bridge and fantail were the surviving members of the crew—fourteen men in all—who had despaired of rescue by surface vessels that were unable to reach the wreck.

But an American Air Rescue H-19 Sikorsky helicopter did get through, in the teeth of driving rains and a 30-knot gale. With all the decks awash and with white water boiling around the base of the smokestack, the fourteen crewmen were taken off with the hoist, one by one, as the H-19 hovered overhead. The effect of this daring rescue was expressed in a simple and eloquent letter received by the commander of the base from which the helicopter had flown:

Tokyo
December 28, 1955

Dear Commander,

This morning I have seen a photograph of relief work of your Group and read the news with deep emotion. I hereby express my heartfelt thanks for your men who saved Japanese seamen from a standpoint of love for humanity. I am not a poet but the following is my improvision [sic]. Please accept my faithful gratitude for your brave behavior.

A rain-storm with thirty-knot gale,
Rush about the northern Sanriku Sea,
On the deck of the Tanda Maru broken in two,
Wait for helping hands covering with rough waters,
Tragic scene is beyond words.
Then a helicopter approaches braving the gale,
A rope of rescue down swaying by the wind,
Cling to a life raft for their lives,
Thus fourteen Japanese seamen were saved,
Ah, calm and heroic Lieutenant Gates.

Sincerely yours,
Kikuju Komori

The saga of the *Tanda Maru* rescue demonstrated, again, the value of a helicopter when surface vessels cannot get to a sinking ship. In the last decade copters have been used this way so frequently that rescues which once might have been thought near miracles are now almost commonplace. However, three years after the *Tanda Maru* a sea rescue took place on the other side of the world which was anything but routine—in the space of less than five hours an Air Rescue crew and their H-19 Sikorsky saved no fewer than forty-eight people from death.

In the gray early morning hours of September 19, 1958, the Portuguese ship *Arnel* had run aground in fog-shrouded home waters. The wreck occurred on shoals off the shore of Santa Maria, an island in the Azores, that archipelago which lies in the Atlantic a thousand miles to the west of Portugal. During the daylight hours that followed, the Air Force H-19 lifted the forty-eight survivors from the ship and placed them safely on a nearby hilltop. The account by the pilot, Air Force Captain Keith Proctor, is one of the most thorough and dramatic descriptions of a rescue operation ever written and is quoted, in part:

> The *Arnel* was part way out of the water, tilting drunkenly on her port side. Huge waves were crashing over the deck, forcing the panic-stricken passengers to hang on for their lives. . . . We had to act fast. . . . I flew around the ship once and came to a hover about 150 feet above the water with the ship on my right. There was a small area on the aft portion of the ship that appeared to be the best place. . . . The area was not large enough to land but by careful maneuvering . . . we were able to hover over the ship and lower a cable to the deck with a rescue basket attached. This was very difficult because the ship was rolling madly on the reef and there was a high mast whipping back and forth forcing me to hover very high. Also, there were several guy wires and considerable rigging across the deck which compelled us to be very careful lowering and raising the basket from the deck so that it would not become entangled.
>
> I could not see the ship from my seat in the cockpit and had to be directed over the exact spot by my hoist operator. He would talk to me constantly over the interphone, saying, "Back, back, hold it, that's good, forward a little, now, left, left, that's good,

49. *A seaman from the* Tanda Maru *dangles on the hoist line below a Sikorsky H-19 Air Force helicopter. In this epic rescue all fourteen survivors were taken off the small vessel, in the face of a 30-knot gale, as it lay sinking off the coast of Japan in December of 1955.*

hold it steady the basket is almost to the deck, the woman is getting in. . . ." This dialogue continued for four and one-half hours while forty-eight men, women, and children were rescued. The only variance would be when our helicopter would get too close to the rigging or mast and then I could tell from the urgency in his voice that reaction had to be fast.

After hoisting each survivor aboard I would fly about one half a mile to a level hill top and deposit my passenger in the waiting arms of the rescue people on the ground. Then we would shoot back to the ship for another pick-up. Our second rescue was that of a woman and two babies . . . the babies slept during the entire operation.

As the day wore on, the constant maneuvering to avoid the whipping mast and to hold the aircraft steady in the right spot for pickup began to tell on the pilot. The mast, especially, was a constant hazard, and it was finally taken down by the ship's crew when they realized the danger. The rest of the narrative, in Captain Proctor's words, describes the struggle:

On one occasion, while hovering over the ship, we made two pick-ups. This did not prove to be a good procedure, however, because I would get so tired that I had considerable difficulty holding the chopper steady. My legs bothered me the most. This was because the wind over the water was very gusty and to hold the helicopter steady demanded constant, heavy rudder pressure.

One other factor that bothered us somewhat was salt spray. Huge breakers would hit the ship and fine salt spray would collect on the helicopter windshield, partially obliterating my vision. This condition was eased somewhat by the presence of rain squalls that would wash away the salt. After rescuing seven women and three babies, our fuel supply was getting dangerously low and we were forced to fly about five miles to Santa Maria Airport to refuel. While precious gasoline was being pumped aboard our helicopter, a Portuguese was asked to write a note to the skipper of the *Arnel* asking him to remove the aft mast from the ship, explaining . . . he would lessen the danger of the helicopter hitting it with the rotor blades. We planned to drop the note to him on our next trip over the ship, but when we arrived, work was already under way removing the mast. Evidently, they also had realized the danger involved.

Decorations are the rule, not the exception, for the helicopter crews of the military rescue services; after this mission they were particularly well-deserved. For his skillful and heroic rescue, Captain Proctor was awarded the Distinguished Flying Cross. His co-pilot and his hoist operator, Lieutenant Gagnon and Sergeant Monnie, received Air Medals. Perhaps the most meaningful comment is the one in the Air Force history of its Air Rescue Service, which calls Proctor's operation "a helicopter masterpiece."

These two missions—the *Tanda Muru* and *Arnel* rescues—are examples of the role being played by the trained specialists and well-equipped aircraft of the military services. But there have been many cases in which the crews of civilian helicopters have also performed magnificently as on-the-spot volunteers. One memorable example occurred in Europe at the nearly completed new $24,000,000 Brussels Airport later in 1958. What happened at Brussels was doubly interesting because it took place at the copter's home base.

Shortly before ten o'clock on the night of November 4, 1958, a worker's kerosene lamp exploded in the unfinished terminal building. In a few minutes, black smoke began to billow from the building. The blaze might be remembered today as nothing more than another unfortunate accident, not uncommon at the site of new construction, except that in the new control tower, which rose 155 feet over the terminal, two men were already on duty. One was Marcel Courtoy, control tower operator, the other signalman Guillaume Michaux.

To the two men in the tower, it seemed at first that the smoke was from the exhausts of an airliner whose engines had just started on the ramp below. But—ominously—as the airplane taxied out toward a runway the smoke did not disappear. It remained and grew stronger, billowing up in thick black clouds.

Courtoy promptly rang up the airport's fire department. Sure that they were not in any real danger, the pair stayed on for a few precious minutes, calling all airplanes with the tower radio, warning them to stay clear of the blazing terminal. Then, only a few minutes later, flames appeared directly under them, and they realized that they were trapped. Escape down the tower stairs was no longer possible, but the roof of the terminal, still untouched by the flames, was only eight feet below the level of the tower, jutting out at right angles to it.

As Courtoy's watch showed 9:56, the smoke became so dense that it was impossible to stay a moment longer. "We're leaving now!" he shouted into the microphone. Then he and the other man made a dash for the rear door and dropped to the terminal's roof. Looking down the sheer face of the structure, they saw the anxious faces of a crowd gathered some 145 feet below. Firemen raised an elevated ladder, but it was a false hope; the ladder was too short. In the dash across the smoldering roof, Courtoy had realized what might be the last chance, and now he played that final card. "Helicopter," he shouted, and Michaux joined in. "Send a helicopter!"

There was no loss of time in getting a copter into the air. Airport people, perhaps more than any other, realize what these aircraft can do. Luckily, Armand Adam, the maintenance boss for Sabena, the Belgian National Airline, was on duty in their hangar; he had called out his crews to help fight the fire and then remained to alert his night shift, due at 10:15.

When he got word at 10:20 that men were trapped on the hangar roof, Adam moved fast. Later, he described the deliberate haste of each move: "We pulled aircraft 00-SHG, the oldest S-58 we have, from the hangar. We removed the two cabin doors, attached a heavy rope on to the cabin seats, and tied a shoulder harness to the rope. This is a safety harness used by our photographer. . . . The idea was to hover over the tower and pick up the men with the harness." His next move was to telephone Gerard Tremerie, chief helicopter pilot for Sabena, who was at his apartment some 6 miles away. Tremerie was there in ten minutes, and just thirty seconds after he leaped from his car the S-58 was airborne, with Adam and a volunteer from the ground crew aboard.

Tremerie flew the helicopter in a slow circle over the burning building as he searched for the two trapped men. It was an eerie, almost nightmarish scene as flames and sparks rose in the night air. Moving in and out of the flickering shadows, the beating rotors reflected patches of ruddy light as the S-58

50. *Hovering on the windward side, the pilot of an Air Force H-43B Huskie maneuvers so the downwash from his rotors will beat back the flames from a burning C-123 transport plane. This crash occurred during an air show at Wilmington, North Carolina, in September, 1961. On the ground at the time, the H-43B was airborne in minutes and played a key role in saving the twelve who survived. The same helicopter later evacuated three critically injured survivors to a hospital. The H-43B, manufactured by Kaman, is a specialized eight-seat crash rescue machine.*

circled, mothlike, about the fire. The pilot checked his wind direction and realized that the hot turbulent air was an added hazard; it would be difficult to hold the copter steady. He abandoned the idea of trying to hover and decided to land on the smoke-shrouded roof instead.

After the first circle, Tremerie spotted the two men huddled at one corner of the roof. Landing carefully, he maintained lift in his rotor so that the full weight of the aircraft was not on the weakened roof. Adam and the other crewman jumped out and hustled the two tower men aboard, and Tremerie promptly put the S-58 into the air and landed in front of the Sabena hangar. The time: 10:35 P.M., only fifteen minutes after Adam had first been told of the trapped men. In another twenty minutes the roof of the terminal was ablaze from end to end. A fast-thinking, fast-moving crew and a helicopter had saved two men from a fiery death.

The civilian pilot-operator who volunteers his aircraft for a spur-of-the-moment rescue frequently is risking his means of making a living as well as his neck, and with no guarantee that anyone is going to foot the bill. A small flying school and charter service (often called a fixed-base operation) is frequently not the most lucrative of enterprises, and one wrecked aircraft may put the operator out of business. Nevertheless, any number of daring helicopter rescues have been accomplished by these pilots.

Of these incidents, in recent years one in particular stands out. This was the rescue operation flown during May of 1960 by pilot Link Luckett, flying a small three-place Hiller 12E from his own charter service—Hill-I-Copters, Inc.—based in Anchorage, Alaska. The rescue actually covered the span of two days, May 20 and 21, and occurred on the slopes of Alaska's Mount McKinley, where mountain climbers John Day and Pete Schoening had been trapped at 18,000 feet. Day had broken his leg, and packing him down the side of the mountain was out of the question. There seemed to be little hope of quick rescue except for the small helicopters of Luckett's service that were based not far away. However, the 18,000-foot level was

51. *Alaskan bush pilot Link Luckett prepares for the extreme cold he will face during the course of a flight made in May of 1960 to rescue two mountain climbers trapped at 18,000 feet on Mount McKinley. Flying a small Hiller 12E from his own air charter service, Luckett managed to rescue both men, one with a broken leg, and was awarded the Carnegie Silver Medal for his heroism.*

well above what was considered to be the top altitude (16,000 feet) to which a 12E could climb.

After stripping one of his ships down, Luckett went for 18,000 feet—a height, incidentally, at which pilots usually need oxygen to fly. The thirty-two-year-old pilot wasn't sure that he could coax the laboring aircraft to rise that high in the thin air. Moreover, for the same reason, he couldn't be sure that it would be possible to take off again, even if the helicopter did manage to reach the two stranded climbers. Nevertheless, against these odds, the Alaskan successfully managed to rescue both men, making six extremely difficult landings and take-offs at 18,000 feet.

For this rescue Luckett was awarded the prized Carnegie Silver Medal, "in recognition of such outstanding heroism." And there was other recognition accorded him. Air Force officials said that it was the highest helicopter rescue operation on record; the altitude had been greater than that of any rescue accomplished by their larger and more powerful machines.

V

Gunships and Troop Carriers

*"Only by exploiting . . . the great potential of flight can we com-
bine complete dispersion in the defense with the facility of
rapidly massing for the counterattack. . . ."*
—JAMES M. GAVIN, Lieutenant General, U.S. Army
from *Army Aviation in the Field Army*, FY-1963
"Get there firstest with the mostest."
—Remark attributed to GEN. NATHAN BEDFORD FORREST,
Army of the Confederacy, 1863

DAWN, VIETNAM. The flight of eleven U.S. Army helicopters
cruises at 90 knots over the lush green jungle, mangrove
swamps, and terraced rice paddies. It is very early, and the
morning air is fresh and calm. The aircraft fly in a loose
formation. The lower ships move in and out of the fast-dis-
appearing shadows of night that still lie along the skyline. The
machines seem to be connected by invisible threads as they
move through the air; the beating rotors rise and fall together
almost as a single unit.

They are not high. When the flight crosses a broad calm river,
the downwash of air from the rotors blows away mist and stirs
the smooth surface. A boat with a woven mat for a sail lies in
midstream. As the helicopters race past, the coarse sail flutters
momentarily in the unexpected breeze and then lies still.

The aircraft cross the river and press on. Below, the rice paddies have disappeared and virgin jungle stretches across the land. The air is no longer smooth. Soon clouds appear; light turbulence is felt, and the pilots jockey and maneuver to hold their positions in the loose formation.

Some of the machines are transports and carry Vietnamese troops, as many as eight of the small soldiers crammed with all their equipment into the tight cabins. Other aircraft bristle with machine guns and rockets clustered on the olive-drab fuselages. There are other weapons for both the transport helicopters and the armed "gunships": two gunners stand at the cabin doors with automatic rifles. When the helicopters reach the Vietcong jungle position to which they are heading, the troop carriers will land and discharge troops, while the heavily armed gunships back them up with machine-gun and rocket fire.

In the cockpits, the pilot and co-pilot of each copter search the jungle horizon for the column of smoke that will mark the point where Vietnamese Air Force airplanes are already attacking. The day is now fully at hand, and the outside air temperature rises rapidly. The flight crews open the cabin ventilators, shift earphones to a more comfortable position, and then methodically prepare their ships for combat.

The first wisp of smoke appears, hanging on the horizon. It grows to a thin striated column, a mixture of different shades and colors. Part of the smoke is the brownish-gray flume caused by high explosive. A greasy black generated by napalm fire bomb shows, as well as other brighter colors: the green, red, and white of the smoke rockets used to mark specific targets. Around the periphery of the smoke, small gnats seem to circle and hang in the humid air.

The helicopters put their noses down and pick up speed for the final dash to the target. Inside the thin aluminum shells the crews and the soldiers tense, waiting for the inevitable slugs that will come whistling up from the Vietcong rifles and machine guns. The gnats grow in size; they have become single-engine attack airplanes that turn and twist, seeking targets on the edge of the clearing that lies below.

Radio communication is now constant and purposeful; words

52. *A twin-rotor U.S. Army H-21 carries Vietnamese soldiers over
a river south of Saigon into battle against Vietcong guerrillas. Behind
it and to the right a smaller and faster UH-1 flies as armed escort,
in the fashion of a destroyer conveying a troopship. Equipped with
rockets and machine guns, the UH-1's were brought into action to
counter ground fire against troop-carrying H-21's. Photo dates from
1963; the H-21 is an older type that is no longer in wide use.*

are not wasted. The armed helicopters spread out to search targets along the edge of the jungle and ask the airplanes to identify the enemy positions. The Vietnamese pilots reply, wanting the helicopters to get the hard ones in close where the planes can't go. The gunships fire long bursts of machine-gun fire and let off salvos of rockets as they circle continuously around the carriers now discharging troops into the tall grass. Swelling the chorus of gunfire and explosion are the weapons of the Vietcong guerrillas; some fire archaic single-shot weapons, while others rake the clearing with modern automatic weapons.

The troop-carrying aircraft have moved in fast. As each helicopter flares out in its flight path and then touches down, the Vietnamese are already clinging to the steps and skids of the machine, anxious to drop off. For these few brief moments, as they poise at the landing spot, the helicopters are exposed and vulnerable: thin-walled targets under the direct fire of the enemy. The safest action is to leave the machine as quickly as possible; before skids touch the ground, the little soldiers boil out of the hatchways, drop off, and sprint into the tall grass. From these hatchways the gunners fire their chattering automatic rifles as fast as they can load, and the spent cartridges go rattling down the sides of the aircraft.

It is a strange combat. The helicopters, and the men leaping from them, are heavily armed; there is fire support from the airplanes circling above as well. Still, the troops are exposed and vulnerable, particularly when the helicopters stop dead still to discharge the soldiers. The Vietcong are well hidden in the jungle; what they lack in gun power they gain in the protection the jungle offers. One helicopter is hit repeatedly and shudders as a string of tracers punch holes in the fuselage and flash through the whirling rotor blades.

Searching for the source of this fire, the pilot of a gunship aims the helicopter like a pistol and looses a series of rockets that go rippling off into the brush; he follows this with long bursts from his machine guns. Leaves are clipped from jungle trees, but the pilot is not sure he has hit anything.

As the last of the Vietnamese troopers move out, the pilots

53. *A North Vietnam postage stamp shows two guerrillas, a man and a woman, firing at a burning United States helicopter. Low-flying aircraft—even jet fighters—are vulnerable to small arms, and the unarmored airplanes and helicopters operated by the U.S. Army in Vietnam have been downed by rifle and machine-gun fire. According to an Army spokesman, approximately fifty of its aircraft, both helicopters and planes, were shot down by ground fire in the four-month period from December of 1964 through March of 1965.*

of the transport ships open their throttles and move their collective pitch-control levers almost as one man. The entire formation rises into the air with the gunners still firing from the open hatches. At this point the transports are most vulnerable: high enough to be clear shots for the guerrillas but without the forward speed needed to throw off their aim. The armed escorts close in and circle the clearing, firing continuously, sending salvo after salvo of rockets and strings of tracer bullets streaking into the jungle.

The transports climb as rapidly as they can to get away from the ground level, moving forward to build up the previous airspeed and helps them gain altitude. As the helicopters rise to over 1,000 feet, the effectiveness of the Vietcong fire thins out; another 500 feet, and it is no longer menacing.

The first part of the mission, the delivery of the raiding party, has been accomplished, and the stage is set for the second phase: a shuttle of armed helicopters from the home base to the combat area. They support the ground troops, searching for the enemy and raking him when they think they see him. When their ammunition is exhausted they fly to home base, rearm, then return for another round.

The "battle" rages throughout the day. It does not follow the rules of conventional warfare—if there are any rules left. The squads thin out, and the fight degenerates into desperate little gunfights in the tall grass and jungle. It is ambush and counterambush. The helicopters support the Vietnamese as closely as they can, but inevitably the areas of toughest resistance, where their firepower is needed most, are the thickest parts of the jungle where the aircraft can do nothing.

Late in the morning, as the sun begins to reach its blinding zenith, the Vietnamese reform in the center of the clearing where the attack had been launched, to prepare for evacuation. The helicopters will assemble and take them out. The results of the fight are inconclusive—no matter the risk, the Vietcong always take their dead with them—but this guerrilla band has at least been scattered. Some prisoners have been taken; supplies and weapons have been captured. As the Vietnamese fall back to the landing zone, an occasional shot is still heard in the jungle. A few guerrillas remain in the area; they will take the risk and get in a few shots at their enemies as they depart.

As the transport machines return, the gunships once again fly in armed circles around the zone. They shoot, but infrequently, more to discourage would-be snipers than anything else. The activity of the morning is reversed as the soldiers take score; the dead and wounded are counted and the losses catalogued by Vietnamese sergeants. In comparison to the furious gunfire of the attack, the liftoff and flight home is an anticlimax, as is the end of most battles.

On the way back the ships fly a ragged formation. The total time for the mission has been over four hours, with much circling and maneuvering within sight and range of riflemen and machine gunners that have been trying hard to hit them. The waist gunners now revert to their other roles and as mechanics and crew chiefs, begin checking the aluminum skin and joints of the airframe for any unnoticed hits. In the cockpits the pilots watch their instruments carefully and fly with extrasensitive touch on controls as they search for signs of damage.

The small formation crosses the same broad flat river it had flown over in the first light of dawn. The river lies dormant in the burning heat of midday. The riverboat has not moved and still lies in the center of the stream; the rough sail hangs still on the slanted mast. Instinctively, in keeping with the ancient tradition of the battleworn, the pilots tighten up and fly a smooth formation. . . .

This narrative of a hit-and-run raid in Vietnam is fictional, but it is based on fact and illustrates the new role of the helicopter in war. No longer merely a reconnaissance and transport aircraft, it has become a weapons platform as well, a gunship that can seek out and destroy a target on the ground.

It was long thought that the helicopter would never be used in this manner. Visionaries and pioneers hopefully conceived of it as an "instrument for saving," a flying machine inherently better suited to the ways of peace rather than war. It was felt that helicopters would always be too slow, too limited in payload and range, too vulnerable to enemy fire. In a more peaceful era this might have remained true. Sadly, the tide of history has caught up with the helicopter and these peaceful hopes. The performance of the newer turbine-powered aircraft has overcome many of the limitations of the earlier machines. In the era of brushfire war, in undeveloped jungle regions where control of the air is not contested, helicopters have come into their own, as both troop carriers and gun platforms.

In this type of operation, the capability of helicopters to operate from small clearings that can be located almost anywhere offers a degree of mobility that cannot be achieved in any other way. To the military, mobility simply means the ability to move troops and firepower quickly to where they are most needed. Aircraft, therefore, can be used for hit-and-run raids and armed-reconnaissance missions, thus assuming the role of light mechanized columns or even the old horse cavalry; it is not surprising that the term "sky cavalry" has been used for this employment of helicopters.

This may be a new technique, but the principle is as old as war itself. It has never been a secret that speed of movement is one of the ingredients necessary to winning a battle. A fatuous young lieutenant, the story goes, once asked Confederate General Nathan Bedford Forrest for the most important rule in warfare. Forrest specialized in running rings around Union horse soldiers, and the junior officer may have expected a lengthy discourse on cavalry tactics. Instead, he got a precise directive on the meaning of mobility, when the General is supposed to have growled, "Dammit, get there firstest with the mostest."

The anecdote is relevant; not a few military strategists have likened the helicopter to a friendly cavalry horse. It is an interesting comparison, although it can be carried to extremes, as in a full-color training film made by the French Army which includes a head-on view of a nineteenth-century Hussar, polished steel helmet, plumes, saber, and all, riding across the landscape. As the furiously galloping cuirassier draws near he

54. *Pilot points straight up prior to quick take-off of a Marine heli-copter from a jungle clearing in April, 1964 as Vietnamese soldiers and American advisers must move fast during a combat resupply mission. Ready for action, machine gunner is on the alert in open hatch. Aircraft is a military version of the Sikorsky S-58, powered by a 1,250-horsepower piston engine. A civilian or military work horse, it can carry 12-18 troops.*

seems to have some strange shapes, possibly wings, growing out of his head. At last the horse and rider jump right over the camera; the wings materialize as the beating rotor blades of an *Alouette* helicopter which had been vibrating along behind him. (One is forced to wonder what the horse thought of all this.)

The inclinations of the French Army notwithstanding, it would be wrong to think of aircraft only in terms of a cavalry role; eventually, the impact on military operations may go far beyond this. Specifically, the U. S. Army has been advancing a new concept, "air mobility," aimed at meeting the threat of limited wars in various parts of the world for years to come. The idea is to replace many of the ground vehicles needed by each division—trucks, jeeps, weapons carriers—in favor of helicopters and other slow-flying aircraft capable of operating from very small airstrips. The concept was summed up in 1963 in this quotation from a U.S. military publication, *Army Aviation in the Field Army,* by then-Lieutenant General James M. Gavin: "Only by exploiting to the utmost the great potential of flight can we combine complete dispersion in the defense with the facility of rapidly massing for the counterattack which today's and tomorrow's army must possess."

The war in Vietnam has seen a quick development of air mobility to a degree that would have seemed impossible a few years ago. The reliance on helicopters has grown steadily; it is estimated that in January of 1966, United States forces had approximately 1,000 in the war zone. Of these, no fewer than 428 aircraft belonged to one unit alone, the unique "Airmobile" First Cavalry Division which has been planned specifically around the mobility of the helicopter. Appropriately dubbed the "Flying Horsemen," the 16,000-man division reached Vietnam in August and September of 1965 as part of American reinforcements. The First Cavalry, plainly, is one stage in the fulfillment of the air mobility concept, and, the performance of its men and its aircraft are sure to serve as a model for similar divisions in the future. Although the unit operates a number of different types, including many short-take-off (STOL) airplanes, two types of helicopters are the mainstay

55. *An Army UH-1 Huey fires 2.75-inch rockets from clusters on each side of the fuselage; its relatively light armament is not always effective against well-concealed jungle positions, however. Powered by a 1,000-horsepower Lycoming T-53 turboshaft engine, top cruise speed is reported to be about 126 miles per hour.*

of its fleet: the UH-1 and the CH-47A, both turbine-powered.*

Most of the division's helicopters are the general-purpose gunship, the UH-1, manufactured by Bell and officially named the *Iroquois* but more often called the *Huey*. Smaller, more maneuverable than the larger transport machines, the single-engine UH-1 is a gun platform and troop carrier which can haul up to eight troops, plus a two-man crew. Ordinarily, the *Huey* is armed with batteries of light rapid-fire machine guns (7.62 caliber) and the smaller 2.75-inch rockets. In the First Cavalry line-up it is the gunship of the team, intended to serve as an armed escort for the transports, and also capable of landing its own troops when necessary.

The considerably larger twin-rotor CH-47A, built by Boeing-Vertol, is a heavyweight transport named the *Chinook*. The twin-engine CH-47A is reported carrying over thirty troops at approximately 138 miles per hour (coincidentally, the useful load seems to be almost the same as the faithful C-47 transport plane of World War II). A particularly useful feature is the ramp at the rear of the fuselage, which can be lowered to permit the loading of vehicles, artillery pieces, or other heavy cargo. The *Chinook* is primarily a transport, but in November of 1965 tests were being made of an armed—and armored—version equipped with a variety of weapons and more than a ton of armor plate.

When airmobile aircraft such as the *Huey* and the *Chinook* are used against guerrillas, this frequently will be in hit-and-run attacks against the enemy's home base—illustrated by the raid described at the beginning of this chapter. The idea, of course, is to build up a quick superiority in a target area and, after accomplishing the mission, to move out before enough force is mustered for a counterattack. The raids are comparable to the Commando operations sometimes carried out during World War II by parachutists. But because helicopters are now available, the raiders can destroy camps, and seize prisoners,

---

* Another significant turbine-powered helicopter in service with the First Cavalry is the very large Sikorsky flying crane, the CH-54A, capable of lifting up to 10 tons. Initially, four CH-54A's accompanied the division to Vietnam. The flying cranes have been used to retrieve downed aircraft, lift portable field hospitals, and to carry 155-millimeter howitzers into combat.

without having to fight their way out on the ground with the odds against them.

However, there are complications to this simple theory. The enemy's exact location must be known, as well as the state of his defenses. This calls for effective espionage and reconnaissance, cooperation of the local population, and other advantages that may not be possible.

Another problem is the vulnerability of today's helicopters to small-arms fire. Structurally these aircraft are no more susceptible to rifle or machine-gun fire than most airplanes. But unlike airplanes flying fast-moving, swooping attack missions, helicopters may be called upon to fight at close range, particularly while landing troops and giving support fire. While landing or hovering they are exposed to direct fire, and it would be a poor rifleman that could not score a hit under these conditions. Although the Army has said that reports of its helicopter losses in Vietnam have been exaggerated out of all proportion, it is nevertheless a fact that more and more armor plate is being planned for its newer aircraft.

Despite these limitations and the more-or-less experimental weapon systems now in use, there is a fundamental military truth about the armed helicopter. It is a flying gun platform that can take its killing equipment almost anywhere and, unlike the airplane, can stop and hover dead still to pick a target with deliberation. There have been recent efforts to create special types of heavily armed and armored airplanes for this work, capable of maneuvering at low speed; indeed, this tradition goes back to the armored trench-strafers of World War I. Nevertheless, by virtue of its ability to hover, the helicopter remains the only aerial gun platform that can close with an enemy on the ground to shoot it out "eyeball to eyeball." Therefore, it should be increasingly important as a means of providing close-in fire support.

To the Army, the turbine-powered aircraft now operating in Vietnam represent a new generation of military helicopters. The introduction of the turbocopters—still under way—marks the change-over from the older, smaller, slower, piston-engined helicopters that have been in service since the days of the

Korean War. Many of these are still in service; examples are the two- and three-seater H-13 *Sioux* and the H-23 *Raven* and the twin-rotor H-21 transport. The H-21, or "Flying Banana," which can carry approximately fifteen troops at about 75 miles per hour and went into service with the Army in 1954, in particular drew criticism in the early stages of the Vietnam conflict as being underpowered and too slow.

The newest approach to the concept of the armed helicopter is the Advanced Aerial Fire Support System (AAFSS), now under development by Lockheed for the Army, which may be in service as early as 1970. The program calls for the design of a large, maneuverable, high-speed aircraft—probably a compound helicopter—which will utilize Lockheed's rigid rotor. An important feature will be its speed, expected to be well over 200 miles per hour, considerably faster than any military helicopter now in service. Armed with the most up-to-date weapons, heavily armored, and equipped with almost every imaginable type of electronic gear for fire control and reconnaissance, the AAFSS—dubbed the "Ayfuss" by the industry—will be a super gunship. Unlike the aircraft in use today, it will be the first Army helicopter designed specifically as a weapons platform for assault missions and for escorting the slower, more vulnerable transports.

Development of the AAFSS illustrates the fact that a crucial element with gunships is the strength and accuracy of firepower they can deliver. Surprisingly, despite the trend toward the super gunship, helicopter armament is still in the experimental stage. The wide range of weapons that have been tested suggests the early days of World War I: automatic rifles and machine guns fired by hand in swinging mounts, or mounted externally and fixed to the airframe, automatic cannon of various calibers, napalm and high-explosive bombs, even the standard heavy 4.5-inch artillery rockets. And this does not include the "special purpose" devices that do not fire projectiles but spray or dispense chemicals.

The machine guns that have been tried include the standard light .30 caliber and the heavy .50 caliber of World War II and

56. *Fearing an explosion, a crewman runs hard to get clear of a burning United States helicopter that has just crashed near the village of Ca Mau on the southern tip of Vietnam. The downed aircraft is the old troop-carrying twin-rotor H-21. It and another crashed during a government raid on a Vietcong area in December, 1962. Despite the seeming vulnerability of helicopters, the Army says they are less susceptible to ground fire than fixed-wing aircraft.*

Korean War vintage.* Another that has been tested—now in service—is the Minigun, a rotating-barrel weapon, with a rapid-fire mechanism that actually originated with the Gatling gun used in the American Civil War. The Minigun has been tested in various calibers, but the one currently in favor uses the newer 7.62-millimeter cartridge which fires a bullet about the same size as the older .30 caliber. The prime advantage of the rotating-barrel weapon is its extremely high rate of fire, one way to cover a wide jungle area where enemy troops are hidden in dense foliage. The 7.62 millimeter Minigun—tried more or less experimentally in Vietnam mounted in pods under the belly of a C-47 transport plane—has a *normal* maximum rate of fire of 6,000 rounds per minute. But there is a disadvantage in the weight of the great quantities of ammunition that must be carried, especially critical with smaller helicopters. Consequently, the weapon most widely used on the UH-1 gunships has been the standard 7.62-millimeter light machine gun with a much lower rate of fire. Ordinarily, several guns are mounted in fixed positions to fire directly forward under the control of the pilot. Although fire from light machine guns is ineffective against troops that are well dug in, the 7.62 seems to be preferred. The gun and its ammunition offer a significant weight advantage over heavier weapons, a prime consideration for smaller aircraft. Since the mission of the gunship, at least of the UH-1, is to provide only "suppressive fire," the light but fairly quick-firing 7.62 is perhaps the best choice for spraying a target area. Another forward-firing weapon used on the *Huey* is the relatively small 2.75-inch rocket, a lightweight projectile as rockets go, apparently chosen for much the same reason as the light machine gun.

Nevertheless, escalation of the war has resulted in increased pressure for heavier armaments. Consequently, in the summer of 1966 the most heavily armed Army gunship in service was the UH-1B model, equipped with the high-rate-of-fire Gatlings, 40-millimeter grenade launchers, and the newer S-11 wire guided missiles that can be aimed—by remote control—on their

* An explanation of the word "caliber," as it applies to guns and rockets, is provided in the Appendix.

way to the target (however, at this time the most common armament for the *Huey* was still the 7.62 machine gun and the 2.75-inch rocket).

The next weapon helicopter planned for the Army line-up is the Bell UH-1H *Hueycobra*, a highly modified two-place version of the UH-1 series. Designed as a heavily armed gunship with sufficient speed to easily escort the fast troop-carrying CH-47 Chinook, the Army's detail specification for the *Hueycobra*, it has been reported, calls for a speed of 146 knots at sea level (about 168 miles per hour). The new gunship features a forward gunner, sitting just in front of the pilot, who fires a remote-control machine-gun chin turret under the nose plus a host of other armaments. With deliveries due to begin in 1967, the UH-1H is considered an interim armed-escort gunship until the AAFSS, mentioned earlier in this chapter, becomes available.

Besides dramatizing the military potential of rotating-wing aircraft, the emergence of the armed helicopter in Vietnam has also drawn attention to the rapid growth of Army aviation. Since the Korean War the Army has been steadily increasing the number of aircraft it operates, training more and more pilots to fly them. In 1955, in particular, a steady program of expansion was begun with the intention of placing more reliance on helicopters than airplanes for air-support functions. Today its aircraft are capable of almost every support role in aerial warfare, including jobs the Air Force once thought exclusively theirs, such as transporting troops and shooting up ground targets. This is best illustrated by comparing the size of Army Aviation with other air forces in the world.[*]

Late in 1964, it had approximately 6,700 aircraft of all types, and of these, the majority—3,800—were helicopters. This meant that it was the world's third largest air force; in first place, obviously, was the United States Air Force, with the Soviet

[*] The terminology is confusing. The present-day U.S. Air Force was the U.S. Army Air Force before 1947. The Army Air Force in turn was descended from the old Army Air Corps; the change-over was made in 1943. What is today called "Army Aviation" began separately, with the use of civilian light airplanes by Army field units in the prewar Louisiana maneuvers held in 1940.

Air Force second. Though opposed by the Air Force, the Army's drive for more and better aircraft is continuing, and it expects to have over 7,000 in 1966, with a fleet of possibly 9,000 by 1970. (This would put in almost on a par with the Air Force). Significantly, it is planned that by 1970 the ratio of helicopters to airplanes will be 7 to 1.

The beginnings of the airmobile concept for the United States Army, and for the Marines as well (Marine helicopters have been in service in Vietnam since the start of the United States commitment), date back to the Korean War. If we overlook the limited operations of World War II, it can be said that helicopters came of military age during the Korean conflict, first for reconnaissance and rescue work and then for use as a troop carrier.

It is not generally appreciated that the U.S. Army has been operating its own aircraft since the earliest days of World War II. The airplanes used then were small two-place machines, fabric covered, that had more in common with first war types than with the heavy bombers and fighters flown by the Air Force during this period. The Army light planes—termed "liaison" aircraft—used for observation, spotting artillery fire, and similar missions, were actually part of the field equipment of the individual battalions and regiments. They were flown by pilots who were officers (and sometimes enlisted men) in these units; the aircraft were operated as closely as possible to the parent units, at times under very primitive conditions.

When the Korean War began, the Army was still saddled with many of its World War II aircraft. One example was the L-4, nothing more than a slightly modified Piper *Cub*. Powered by a 65-horsepower engine, at full throttle it could manage a top speed of just over 80 miles per hour. Eventually, the pressures of the Korean conflict, coupled with the inadequacy of the existing equipment, led to a re-equipping with up-to-date aircraft and to the introduction of the helicopter.

The Army's use of helicopters in Korea began during that first terrible winter of retreat in 1950, when small Bell H-13's were shipped in. Up to this point the work of patrol and observation was being handled by the liaison airplanes. Besides

57. *A small two-place Bell helicopter, the H-13 Sioux (civilian designation, Model 47), was used by the U.S. Army during the Korean War together with the comparable two-place Hiller H-23 Raven. Both were powered by engines of 200 horsepower and cruised at about 80 miles per hour. H-13's were in service early in 1951; when used for medical evacuation, litters were attached to the sides of the fuselage. Other missions for H-13's included observation, reconnaissance, and wire laying. Later models are still in service.*

the two-seater light planes, *Cubs* and *Aeroncas,* there was also the considerably more powerful and more useful wood-wing Stinson L-5; it had a 185-horsepower engine. Unhappily, some of the L-5's had engines so badly worn they became unsafe to fly (The writer has first-hand knowledge of this; he was a crew chief for two of these worn-out L-5's). Later, many of these airplanes were replaced by all-metal Cessna L-19's and a few small copters. Described in Chapter IV, one of the first battle-field evacuation missions by Army helicopter was flown in January of 1951 by Captain Albert C. Seburn, Commander of the 2nd Army Helicopter Detachment.

During the winter, spring, and early summer of 1951 the crucial battles of the war were fought as the Chinese attempted to overwhelm the revitalized United Nations army. Increasingly, helicopters were used by battlefield commanders who wished to make a close surveillance and needed to land right in the combat area. In this role they were plainly superior to the light planes.

An example of this was the incident on May 17 during the bloody "May Massacre." At this time the Chinese were trying to crush the United Nations line by sheer force of numbers with waves of troops thrown against rolling barrages of artillery fire. During a twenty-four-hour period 30,000 shells were fired, more than had ever been fired before by American artillery in one day's time. In one area, Division Commander Clark L. Ruffner sent the Dutch Battalion to close a gap in the line near a town called Sapkyo-ri. Ruffner himself went in close in an H-13 as the Dutch began their attack. Dodging small-arms fire, the pilot took advantage of every nook and cranny of the rugged mountain terrain. The small helicopter remained untouched by Chinese bullets, but at three o'clock in the afternoon, at the height of the attack, the engine quit cold. The aircraft smashed into a rocky spur and rolled over, splintering its wood rotor blades, almost in the sight of the enemy. Miraculously, General Ruffner and the pilot suffered only bruises.

After the summer of 1951 the shifting battle line was stabilized in the rugged mountainous terrain of central Korea. In this part of the front, in September and October, the first tests of the helicopter's ability to carry troops into inaccessible areas in a combat zone were made by the Marine First Division, when it airlifted an entire battalion to a spot on a remote ridge. Considering how important rotating-wing aircraft are today to Army plans for airborne assault, it is interesting that these historic tests were made instead not by the Army but by the U.S. Marines. Two separate experimental missions, "Windmill I" and "Windmill II," were initiated with Sikorsky HRS-1 transport helicopters (similar to the civilian S-55) each capable of carrying ten soldiers. The first operation, Windmill I, on September 13, was in an area of the Korean mountains extending from Inje to the Punch Bowl battle zone and involved some twenty-eight flights in a period of a little over fourteen hours. The weight of supplies flown in was approximately 9 tons, with the helicopters landing on ridges 2,100 feet above sea level. On return trips the aircraft flew out seventy-five wounded men. The second operation in the same general area, Windmill II, was slightly less ambitious: just over 6 tons, hauled by ten helicopters. With justifiable pride, the Corps Historical Branch said of the operation: "Tactical history was created by the Division . . . In September and October 1951, a glimpse of future warfare was given when Marine helicopter lifts on a company scale led to the lift of an entire battalion with its equipment."

VI

V/STOL's:
The Shape of Things to Come

"No matter how weird the concept, flight success has followed in almost all of these developments—tail sitter, wire sitter, tilt wing, ducted fans, underfoot rotors, power jet VTOLs, and even 'flying saucers.' This period has truly proved that 'given enough power, one can fly (or hover) a barn door.'"*
                               —RALPH P. ALEX, President
                          American Helicopter Society (1959)

AFTER WORLD WAR II the design and shape of the helicopter became standardized on a few basic configurations that, for the most part, actually dated from the prewar period. And although they have been greatly improved and refined, these same designs still predominate today.

However, in the last few years the situation has changed to become one of those rare and fascinating periods in aviation history when really new types of aircraft are being created: vertical-rising machines, some related to the helicopter, some not, that can rival or surpass it in its own element. The shapes are fluid and not closely defined—the helicopter that flies today with a main rotor whirling over an uncluttered fuselage may soon sprout airplane-type wings, a propeller, even tail surfaces. In contrast to the design of airplanes, which have grown so

* Quoted from an editorial which appeared in the July, 1959, issue of *The Journal of the American Helicopter Society.*

much alike that it is increasingly difficult to tell the product of one design team from another, there is almost bewildering variety in the line-up of the new aircraft.

Nor have all the new developments caused a change in the outward appearance of helicopters or resulted in the creation of new types; many of the changes have been internal, not external. The widespread use of turboshaft engines in place of the older piston engines is one example. The turbine power plants are a big leap forward, superior because they weigh less per horsepower and have fewer working parts than a piston engine. By way of comparison, a turbine engine used in one of today's large helicopters that produces 1,200 horse-power will weigh less than half—and take up only half the space—of a piston-and-crankshaft engine of only 1,000 horse-power.

Among other hidden improvements to the standard heli-copter are the new types of rotor systems that are intended to increase top speed, improve control, or—hopefully—to lower the cost of the machine. At the top of the list, perhaps, are the stiffened blades of Lockheed's rigid rotor, indicating an im-provement in top speed in forward flight. Since this is a radical departure from the traditional free-and-easy articulated rotor that lets the blades pivot on hinges in almost any direction, the new system has also been termed a "hingeless" rotor. Still another recent improvement is the "door hinge" hub, perfected by Bell, that represents a simplification of the rotorhead mechanism. The designers call it this because the moving parts, they say, are hardly more complex than a brass door hinge.

Perhaps the most intensive research has concerned the Archilles heel of the helicopter, its limited top speed. Although a powered rotor remains the best aerodynamic system for hauling a flying machine straight up into the air, once it is in forward flight the situation changes considerably. The rotor then creates its own self-induced drag holding down the speed of the helicopter, which if forced through the air may become unmanageable.

The search for a solution to this and other dilemmas inherent in helicopter design has been coupled with growing military interest in large, fast, long-range vertical-rising aircraft that can operate from small unprepared landing areas. The result, in the last ten years or so, has been the emergence of a whole new group of vertical risers, of which the helicopter is only one among many. The catch-all term generally used to describe these machines is the capital-letter abbreviation "V/STOL" for "Vertical/Short Take-Off and Landing" aircraft.

The helicopter is the oldest member of the V/STOL family (it was in use years before the term itself was invented); consequently much of the interest in V/STOL's today is concerned with aircraft intended as improvements of the helicopter. Some are helicopter configurations to which a propeller or jet engine has been added for forward propulsion in company with a small lifting wing (the compound helicopters). Others are a new breed of overpowered airplanes that can tilt propellers or lift-fan rotors straight up for vertical flight and straight ahead for forward flight. Still others are airplanes that rise vertically supported by the thrust or flow from powerful jet engines.

There seems to be almost as many different ways to describe V/STOL's as there are types of aircraft that might be so designated. But for all practical purposes we can content ourselves with a general description of the two different parts of the V/STOL puzzle: the VTOL's and the STOL's.

VTOL's (Vertical Take-Off and Landing) are all those machines including the helicopter, that have the ability to rise or descend vertically and to hover in midair. They include all the major types that have already been mentioned—compound helicopter, tilt-prop and tilt-wing, jet VTOL—and a few other more exotic specimens as well. It is significant that almost all the VTOL's are also capable of making a running take-off that requires only the shortest of runways. In fact, when space is available the runing take-off is always preferred, since it is less of a strain on the aircraft and the engines and permits a greater payload. The VTOL's also have the ability to reverse the maneuvers described here—that is, to land by descending vertically or by making a running landing with a very short forward roll. It should be noted that only the oldest of the VTOL's, the well-tried helicopter, has ever been in regular service, at least up to the date of this writing. Despite years of research and testing, the other aircraft are still in the trial stage.

STOL (Short Take-Off and Landing) aircraft, on the other hand, are simply specialized fixed-wing airplanes, unrelated to helicopters or other vertical risers, designed with aerodynamic features that provide high lift and good control at very low airspeeds. The STOL's can take off and land at extreme angles and require only the shortest of runways; for some of the smaller machines as little as 200 or 300 feet may be enough. During take-off the STOL airplane requires only a short run in order to reach the low airspeed at which its wing will begin to lift. While landing, a STOL can fly so slowly, without stalling, that when it touches down it can be stopped easily after a short forward roll. The STOL's, as a class, are not to be considered as experimental aircraft; numbers of them are in production in various parts of the world. Nor is the concept especially new. The small Ryan *Dragonfly* built for the U.S. Army in 1940 was an effective STOL airplane, as was the Fieseler *Storch* used by the Germans in World War II.

There are many advantages to the STOL airplane. It is less complicated and therefore less expensive than VTOL aircraft. The wings are fixed, and there are no rotors or tilting propellers —no pivoting or rotating systems such as those needed for the vertical flight of the VTOL's. But it is seriously lacking in one critical area: it is incapable of vertical flight or hovering and must always keep moving in order to keep flying, however slowly. The larger STOL's for example, could be expected to require at least 60 miles per hour of airspeed during an approach. In addition, the STOL has to have a runway of sorts on which to land, and, perhaps more important, it must have an adequate amount of clear airspace in which to maneuver and line up on the runway.

Returning to the VTOL's, the true vertical-risers, we find that, despite their very great differences in outward appearance. by limiting ourselves to important developments we can reduce

TYPICAL VTOL PROPULSION SYSTEMS

	VTOL	CONVENTIONAL FLIGHT	REMARKS
HELICOPTER	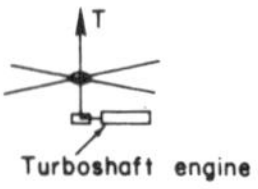 Turboshaft engine	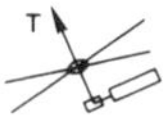	Illustration represents a conventional helicopter with the rotor being driven by a turboshaft engine.
COMPOUND HELICOPTER	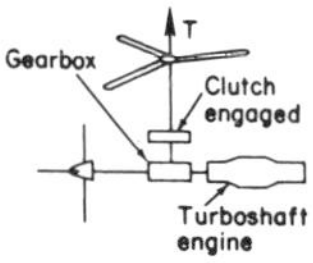 Gearbox — Clutch engaged — Turboshaft engine — Propeller in low pitch	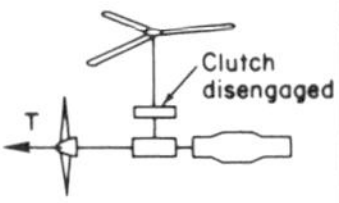 Clutch disengaged — Propeller in high pitch	A mechanical-driven rotor is shown, similar to the system used on the Piasecki 16H-1A. An older type was the Fairey Rotodyne, which used the same principle but employed pressure jets at the blade tips to drive the rotor.
TILT-PROP AIRPLANES	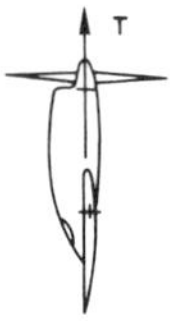	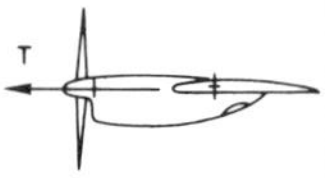	On this type the wing tilts simultaneously with the propellers. The Vought-Hiller-Ryan XC-142A is an example.
TILT-PROP AIRPLANES	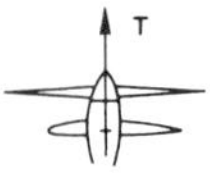	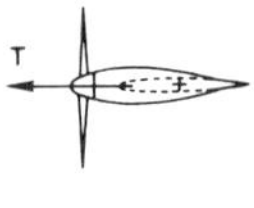	Curtis Wright X-19 is an example of this type of aircraft--the propellers tilt while the wing remains fixed in position.
JET VTOL	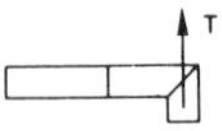		Simple jet engine with thrust deflector is shown, as used on the Bell X-14.

NOTE: "T" Indicates THRUST

58. The chart shows examples of various propulsion systems used for vertical take-off and landing (VTOL) aircraft. The illustrations in the column at the left indicate how the thrust for vertical flight is achieved; in the center column is shown the thrust force that propels the aircraft horizontally through the air.

59. The Bréguet 941 is a four-engine turbine-powered STOL airplane used by the French Air Force since 1961. Technical features include full-span flaps, drive shafts linking all four engines so all props will keep turning if one engine fails, as well as other systems to aid STOL operation. Advantages claimed for this aircraft (as compared to a VTOL) include simplicity of design, payload and speed equal to a standard fixed-wing airplane, plus excellent short take-off and landing characteristics. According to the manufacturer, the 941 cruises at 300 miles per hour and is capable of taking off in 820 feet over a 50-foot obstacle while carrying a 15,000-pound payload.

them to four primary types: standard helicopter, compound helicopter, tilt-prop airplane, and jet VTOL. Each of the four will be discussed in turn, with an eye to the method by which each achieves vertical flight and its individual advantages and disadvantages.

First in the line-up is the *standard helicopter*. With this aircraft, the rotor is the heart of the flight mechanism, actually serving two purposes: it provides the direct lift needed to make the machine rise vertically and to support the ship in flight, and at the same time, by "leaning forward" slightly, it propels the craft through the air. The helicopter is superior to other VTOL's in its ability to pull itself straight up or to hover in the air; it is primarily a direct-rising and hovering aircraft. This is owing to the fact that a helicopter rotor offers the lowest thrust-to-weight ratio for vertical take-off of all the various VTOL types; it can lift the most weight for the least amount of engine power. However, the copter has to pay for its superiority as a hovering machine; it is the slowest of all the VTOL's. The fastest speed to be expected of a helicopter with a conventional rotor system—even the most powerful of the turbine-powered machines—is rarely over 200 miles per hour. (In July of 1963 a large French helicopter, the Sud-Aviation *Super Frelon* powered by three turboshaft engines, was driven hard over a short course to set a world's speed record of 217.7 miles per hour.) The problem is that when the high speed limit of the helicopter is reached, a phenomenon termed "blade stall" occurs. This creates so much extra drag that a great deal of extra power is required, excessive vibration may be experienced, and there will be a troublesome—if not dangerous—loss in control as well (an explanation of blade stall is furnished in the Appendix). This is not to say that ultimately new rotor systems may not be developed to the point where this limitation can be overcome; considerable research has been underway in this area. Another point to be considered is that if some form of direct thrust is provided—such as added jet engines mounted on the fuselage—the aircraft may then be forced to higher speeds despite the limitations of blade stall.

A variation of the standard helicopter is the *compound heli-*

copter, of which the promising but never-utilized Fairey *Roto-dyne* (described in Chapter III), flown in Britain in the late 1950's—a large machine intended for airline service—is an example. In the last few years there has been a revival of interest in the compound type, basically a standard helicopter re-designed with a propeller (or a jet engine) to give it added push; usually a small lifting wing is also part of the configuration. The rotor is used for vertical take-off; after reaching altitude, power to the rotor is then reduced or stopped entirely and it is allowed to freewheel as the ship goes into forward flight. With the rotor thus unloaded it is possible to obtain a cruise speed considerably greater than that attainable with the rotor under power. For vertical descent, the rotor is clutched in and, in effect, the machine in converted back to a helicopter. The compound helicopter can be thought of as a kind of helicopter that can partially convert while in flight to an airplane configuration by unloading the rotor. The intention, of course, is to combine the superior vertical flight and hovering characteristics of the helicopter with the high cruise speed available from use of an unloaded rotor. However, in some ways the compound helicopter has to pay for its higher rate of speed: There is a decrease in its vertical take-off and hovering capability, since the wing interferes with the airflow through the rotor; then, too, the added weight of this structure reduces the payload.

The third type in our parade of VTOL's is the *tilt-prop airplane,* a complete break from the tradition of the helicopter. If the compound helicopter can be thought of as a kind of helicopter that can partially turn itself into an airplane, the tilt-prop machines may be considered as airplanes that have the ability to turn into helicopters. The tilt-prop, basically, is an airplane that has oversized propellers, or fanlike rotors, mounted on pivots so they can be shifted to point either straight up or straight ahead. With some aircraft of this type the wings tilt along with the propeller, and these have been referred to as "tilt-wings." The term tilt-prop is perhaps more suitable, since it covers both configurations. The tilt-prop airplanes have no rotors, there is only a small wing to support the machine in

60. World's first successful Quadrotor or twin-tandem helicopter was Convertawings Model A, shown here during test flights at Zahn's Airport, Amityville, New York, in March of 1956 with designer D. H. Kaplan at the controls. This machine, described in Chapter III, was the test bed for a unique method of control that used no cyclic changes and incorporated simplified hubs with strap-mounted rotor blades, a form of "hingeless" rotor. It was a forerunner of current VTOL designs that use tandem wings or a square array of four fans, ducts, or jets.

61. *Experimental XV-3, a vertical take-off aircraft with tilting rotors, is shown hovering at the Bell Aircraft Corporation's Fort Worth plant. The XV-3, first flown in 1955, had two rotors mounted at the tips of a small fixed wing; the rotors (or propellers) could tilt from the vertical position to straight ahead for forward flight. The rotors were wide in diameter—23 feet across—resembling those of a helicopter. Maximum speed of the XV-3 was reported as 150 knots (about 173 miles per hour).*

62. *New four-engine tilt-wing XC-142 built by Ling-Temco-Vought (with Hiller and Ryan as subcontractors) is shown during field trials at Edwards Air Force Base, California, as the aircraft rises vertically from the runway and then goes into forward flight. The XC-142 was the first United States V/STOL to progress beyond the experimental stage to actual field trials, which began at Edwards in July, 1965; it flew 1,200 miles in course of delivery. According to the manufacturers, the troop-carrying XC-142 is designed to lift 8,000 pounds of payload vertically and can handle an additional 4,000 pounds when operated as a STOL airplane; estimated top speed is over 400 miles per hour. With aircraft of this type, the propellers can be pivoted to point straight upward for vertical take-off or straight ahead for flight in the airplane configuration.*

forward flight. The reason for this design approach, again, is to achieve higher speed than with the helicopter. The tilt-prop designs are another step forward on the speed scale; the large ones should be capable of cruising speeds in the 300- to 400-mile-per-hour range, perhaps more. However, at this time they seem to be inferior to both the helicopter and compound helicopter in vertical take-off and in hovering ability; their propellers are not as efficient as rotor systems. Presumably, control in hovering flight may not be as good, and the payload that can be lifted vertically much less (for the same power) than with a helicopter. Another point to be considered is that the vertical take-off of the tilt-prop can be more of a strain on the engines than it would be with a helicopter.

The last type we will consider is the *jet VTOL,* basically a jet airplane with the ability to rise vertically. A number of aircraft of this type are currently in various stages of development. All have one important point in common: in order to rise vertically the flow from the turbojet engines is directed downward so a lifting force is created.* Since all are jets, these aircraft are the fastest of any of the VTOL's, in fact, several reconnaissance-fighter airplanes have been built along these lines. However, most jet VTOL designs—particularly those intended for development into transport-type aircraft—are still in the experimental stage, are complex, and generally do not have lift-off and hovering characteristics that are equal to the helicopter or other VTOL's.

Each of these VTOL types represents a different compromise between the ability to rise vertically, lifting the most weight for the least power, and the ability to cruise at a high forward speed. At one end of the spectrum we have the helicopter. Because of the superior lifting capability of its rotor, which provides the most lift for the least power—as compared to the other VTOL systems—the copter is the best hovering

---

* There are exceptions. One significant example is Ryan's "lift-fan" XV-5A which has a type of shrouded rotor, or fan, in each wing. For vertical flight the flow from turbojet engines is used to drive the fans. If the fans are thought of as a special form of propeller, the XV-5A can be considered as a type of propeller VTOL. For forward flight, flow from the turbojets is directed to the rear and the XV-5A is propelled in same manner as any jet aircraft. Built along fighter plane lines, it has been reported as capable of speeds of over 500 miles per hour.

and lift-off machine. However, because of the high drag created by the rotor when in forward flight, it has relatively poor speed. At the other end of the spectrum we have the tilt-prop airplanes, where the situation is reversed. And then, more or less in between (though closely related to the helicopter) we have the compound helicopter, which has a lift-off capability nearly equal to the standard helicopter but a top speed that is considerably greater.

Concerning the lift-off and hovering characteristics of the new VTOL types, there is one sobering fact to be considered. These aircraft are completely dependent upon the perfect functioning of their engines and control systems, unlike the helicopter (or compound helicopter) which has an inherent safety factor in the autorotational capability of the rotor. If a serious power failure or a failure in the control system is experienced while the VTOL is being supported by the thrust from its engines, obviously, a crash is almost inevitable. In the last few years there have been several disastrous crashes of experimental VTOL's (a tilt-prop, a lift-fan, and a jet) due to trouble while the aircraft was in the slow flight or hovering condition.

An important characteristic of most VTOL's is their capability for STOL operations from short runways while making airplane-type running take-offs and landings. When operating this way, they can take off and climb out at quite severe angles, using little runway, with high payloads and without placing undue strain on the engines. This is true of the helicopter, compound helicopter, and the tilt-prop. Of these three types of VTOL's, the new tilt-props are the aircraft that might stand to benefit most from the STOL type of operation. They are the fastest in forward flight and therefore offer the most from the viewpoint of speed and range. However, they seem to be the poorest hovering machines of the three types and might be operated as short take-off airplanes—with the propellers in the horizontal position—whenever possible with certain important benefits. The vertical take-off ability could then be saved for special situations where it would be needed. This might be where a take-off would be made in the short take-off airplane configuration with a maximum gross payload. At the end of

63. *British Hawker-Siddeley P.1127 jet VTOL tactical fighter is shown hovering aboard aircraft carrier H.M.S. Ark Royal during 1963 trials. Aircraft is powered with a Bristol-Siddeley Pegasus lift-thrust turbofan engine designed with four discharge nozzles that can be rotated to provide either vertical or horizontal thrust. For vertical flight and hovering, the nozzles are pointed so that the engine's flow is downward (nozzles are visible under the wing). For forward flight the nozzles are rotated to face directly to the rear. Control in vertical flight and hovering is accomplished by means of reaction jets in the nose, at each wing tip, and in the tail. The airplane has exceeded the speed of sound in forward flight at altitude, has flown at 65 miles per hour sideways and over 25 miles per hour backwards. In the spring of 1966, the P.1127 was under evaluation by the U.S. Army.*

the flight after enough fuel had been used up, the ship might then be light enough to make a vertical descent landing easily at a heliport.

This description of how a tilt-prop VTOL might be operated as a short take-off airplane in order to increase its payload touches on a crucial point: the question of whether these aircraft have any reasonable chance of economic survival, particularly if they are used for carrying passengers in scheduled service. The outstanding fact that has been learned from the experience of most helicopter airlines in the last decade is that operating costs are too high; as a result, fares are too high and passenger volumes too small. Whether faster, larger VTOL's and STOL's are the answer, or even part of the answer, remains to be seen. For the most part, the development of these aircraft has been funded by the military, and they have been designed for military requirements. This consideration, as well as many economic and technical factors, makes it impossible to do justice to the question here. It may be helpful, however, to outline a few of the important technological trends now under way.

One trend is toward an increase in the size of transport helicopters, for very much the same reason that transport airplanes have grown steadily in size in the last twenty to thirty years. All things being equal, the larger the helicopter, the lower the cost per seat mile; the cost of operating new, larger aircraft ordinarily does not rise in the same proportion as the increase in passenger capacity. A forty-passenger helicopter can operate with only a pilot and co-pilot—exactly the same number of flight crew members as a twenty-passenger machine. Here, the capacity has doubled, but the crew cost is the same.

Another basic trend, as we have noted, is the consistent effort to reduce drag so that a higher cruise speed is possible, while retaining the high-lift capability needed for vertical take-off and hovering. The examples that have been mentioned include the compound helicopter, with its freewheeling rotor and additional means of thrust (an interesting recent development is Sikorsky's experimental swing-tail Rotoprop—the tail rotor pivots to face to the rear and provides forward thrust by

64. One trend in the design of transport helicopters is a growth in size, since operating costs do not rise in the same proportion. This artist's sketch of a very large "next-generation" passenger helicopter operating from a futuristic city heliport bears some resemblance to the Sikorsky CH-53A, a large military helicopter that carries a payload of 4 tons (thirty-eight troops) at a cruise speed of approximately 170 miles per hour.

serving as a propeller); the tilt-prop airplanes that can convert to a low-drag high-speed airplane configuration for forward flight; and the jet VTOL airplanes. Any number of other experimental configurations have been proposed, and several involve the complex *stopped-rotor* concept. This would consist of an aircraft furnished with a lifting wing in combination with a rotor that could be slowed down, and then stopped entirely while in flight. For high forward speed the rotor would then form a fixed lifting surface—an approach very much the same as that intended for the Herrick *Convertoplane* of 1937 described in Chapter II. Still another somewhat similar —though more complicated—approach would have the rotor stopped, the blades neatly folded and trailed aft in a streamline position, and then the entire bundle stowed away in the top of the fuselage while the aircraft sped along on the lift of its wing.

There has also been a particularly strong engineering effort in another area: the creation of new turboshaft engines that are lighter and more powerful—in other words, the most power for the least weight. This, of course, benefits any type of aircraft, but it is particularly vital for VTOL machines that need great levels of thrust for a take-off that is a direct struggle against gravity. Part of the engine designer's problem is that the vast power needed for take-off is not needed for an economic cruise speed. Then, too, there is the fact that turbojet engines run best at full throttle; they cannot run with any efficiency at partial power settings. For this reason various VTOL designs have been proposed with ultra-lightweight extra engines to be run at full power at take-off and landing and then shut down completely during cruise flight

VII

Helicopter Airlines

"The whole helicopter industry is primarily a group of time merchants. Everything related to helicopters can be broken down into a time factor. . . .

"In congested area application . . . the savings are sometimes not quite so obvious as they might appear. People used to the speed of air travel sometimes forget to count the minutes they spend going to and from airports."

—J. H. ORPEN, Export Sales Manager,
Bell Helicopter Company (1963)

HELICOPTERS, even the largest and most powerful ones flying today, are relatively slow and limited in payload and range when compared with the conventional airplanes used by regular airlines. But obviously they do have one key advantage over fixed-wing aircraft: the ability to take off and land vertically—straight up and straight down—and thus operate from very small, restricted areas. Furthermore, if their top speed is slow, it is still immeasurably faster than any form of surface vehicle. Therefore, almost since the time the first practical helicopters appeared on the scene, there have been efforts to provide regular air transportation on short-haul routes in densely populated areas where there is no room for full-sized airports. Scheduled airline-type operations began a few years after the end of World War II. Since then the industry has been striving for a real break-through—helicopter transportation on a large scale in, around, and over major cities in the United States.

But the development of this kind of service, for the most part, has been slow, even disappointing. In several cities (including New York, Chicago, Los Angeles, San Francisco) small helicopter airlines have been struggling for many years to make ends meet. These operations usually consist of scheduled flights between a few strategically located heliports in the city or its outskirts and the important airports near the city. Considering the relatively small number of passengers and flights and the few aircraft involved, these helicopter lines are reminiscent of the pioneer fixed-wing airlines of thirty years ago.

Despite years of government subsidies, introduction of big turbine-powered aircraft, and growing public acceptance, the picture is still not encouraging. And one of the basic reasons is that the helicopter lines just haven't been able to get enough passengers; their operating costs are too great, and therefore the fares are relatively high in comparison with ground transportation. Does the industry feel that the future will be any brighter? The answer seems to be a cautious "yes"—there are new potential markets, more efficient ways of using aircraft, improved types of helicopters, and other indications that better days may be coming.

In part, the reasons for this hopeful view stem from the advantages (and disadvantages) inherent to certain route patterns. There are other factors, of course, but an inquiry into these patterns will also help to illustrate exactly what kind of service can be provided by a helicopter passenger line. The basic routes flown by existing operators in the United States fall into three important categories: flights between downtown heliports and outlying airports, flights from one airport to another, and flights from one heliport to another, across a network of heliports in one area.

Flights between downtown areas and outlying airports, the first category, of course are intended for air travelers who want fast transportation to and from the terminals. The experience of the existing helicopter airlines indicates that a real market exists here—particularly among people on business trips—that

1910

" PIGEON-HOUSES ? "
" NO, AERO-GARAGES."

65. *This cartoon from the March 4, 1909, issue of the old* Life *maga-zine predicted "aero-garages" on the tops of tall buildings. Marked as a "real estate number," the issue devoted space to contemplating how the newly invented flying machine would affect New York. Over half a century later, the prophecy is beginning to materialize with the development of downtown city heliports.*

66. *The ability to fly from the heart of the city seems to be part of the dream of an ultimate* Megalopolis. *In this eerie scene from the classic German film* Metropolis, *made by Fritz Lang in the 1920's, futuristic aircraft fly from massive downtown buildings. Although the pilot was primitive, remarkable effects such as this were produced through use of models.*

67. *The first regularly scheduled helicopter passenger service in the world was pioneered by British European Airways on June 1, 1950 between Liverpool and Cardiff with Westland-Sikorsky S-51's. Here, one of those BEA S-51's is shown at London's Northolt Airport. The Liverpool-Cardiff service was operated for a year on a trial basis and later transferred to other routes in Britain. Apparently the operation was unprofitable, and from 1956 to 1964 scheduled service ceased, although charter work continued. In May, 1964, BEA reintroduced scheduled flights on the short Land's End - Isles of Scilly route with twenty-five passenger Sikorsky S-61's.*

has not yet been tapped. The reasons for this are complex. Part of the problem is the fairly high fares, which the lines hope to reduce when new, faster, larger (and therefore more profitable) aircraft become available. Other hopes are based upon closer connections and tie-ins with airline flights and more strategically located heliports, such as those planned for the roofs of airline terminals. Another important factor is simply the great increase expected in the number of airline passengers in the next few years which, obviously, should result in more fares for the helicopter lines.

Helicopter lines have found the profit picture to be more encouraging with respect to the second category of service, the airport-to-airport flights serving as a connecting link between airlines at sister airports near the same community. This kind of operation is most effective and most attractive to passengers when it connects airports that are fairly distant from one another and located so that an obstacle such as the mass of a city or a wide body of water lies in between. In this situation, surface transportation by limousine, coach, taxi, or boat may be so time-consuming that passengers will find the charms of the helicopter to be irresistible. One example is the service provided by New York Airways from Newark Airport, located to the west of Manhattan, over the heart of the city to the Long Island airports on the other side.

Another is the service of the San Francisco and Oakland Helicopter Airlines, which flies a cross-bay operation between San Francisco International Airport and Oakland Municipal Airport. It is interesting to note that the California carrier has been operating a new kind of air vehicle on this overwater route, a British-made "hovercraft" or ground-effect machine which rides on an air cushion generated by turbine-powered fans.

The third category, flights between a network of heliports, would be aimed at a mass commuter market, the kind of "flying bus" operation that helicopter adherents ten or fifteen years ago were predicting would be the next revolutionary step in air transportation. Unquestionably, many dwellers in the land of suburbia and exurbia would like nothing better than regular point-to-point air transportation from their communities to downtown city centers—but it can't be provided cheaply enough with existing aircraft, although considerable effort has been put into trying to work out some arrangement that would make the helicopter a viable tool for this commuter market. The problem, of course, is tied to the two big passenger movements—in opposite directions—every working day. Any attempt to put copters into this service would mean the aircraft would be idle for most of the day, unless some other use could be found. One approach, proposed by Sikorsky Aircraft, would utilize their S-64A Skycrane. The idea calls for the use of a detachable passenger pod (referred to in the industry, naturally, as a "purple people pod"). The pod would be used during the morning and evening rush hours and could be removed during the day so the helicopter could be free to do other work as a "prime mover."* Sikorsky has conducted tests of the S-64A for work in the movement of freight from ships and docks and for other flying crane applications. The tests were encouraging, indicating that speed in handling cargo of this sort might offset the high operating cost.

A similar application of the flying crane concept was demonstrated by the Soviets at the 1965 Paris Air Show with the unveiling of their Mil Mi-10. An enormous machine with a single main rotor, the Mi-10 was developed from the equally large Mi-6 (both aircraft are powered by two turboshaft engines giving a total power of 11,000 shaft horsepower). The Russians have claimed several new payload-to-altitude records for the Mi-10, including the lifting of 55,346 pounds—more than 27 tons—to an altitude of over 9,000 feet. The normal payload, however, would be much less, approximately 33,000 pounds. During the show the Mi-10 carried a small bus under its fuselage between long stiltlike landing gear struts.

Another proposal for a successful helicopter airline service, still in the planning stage, concerns an entirely different kind

* An operation of this sort is envisioned in a proposal advanced by the Los Angeles City Department of Airports. Sikorsky S-64's would be used to transport pods, capable of holding 60 to 70 passengers, between downtown areas and Los Angeles International Airport. After being detached from the helicopter, the pod would be joined to a tractor-trailer and the unit would then serve as a surface bus.

68. A Sikorsky S-60 Skycrane demonstrates its load-carrying ability by hauling a large stripped-down S-58 (Army designation, CH-34), which weighs approximately 4 tons empty. This large flying crane (main rotor diameter, 72 feet) first flew in March of 1959, powered by two Pratt and Whitney turboshafts of 2,100 horsepower each. From it was developed the production-model Skycrane, the S-64A, with twice the power (two turboshafts of 4,620 horsepower each), designated the CH-54A by the U.S. Army and capable of lifting up to 10 tons.

69. A twin-rotor Boeing-Vertol V-107 flies past the mouth of New York's East River, with the Brooklyn Bridge and the tip of Manhattan in the background. Powered by two CT-58 turboshaft engines (together they produce 2,500 horsepower), the V-107 is operated by New York Airways in scheduled flights over the city. It can cruise at speeds up to 150 miles per hour, carries 25 passengers, and operates from land or water; the fuselage has a watertight hull bottom in addition to wheel alighting gear. U.S. Army version of V-107 is the CH-46.

of route structure, which might open a new and profitable market: a direct operation from the downtown area of one major city to the downtown area of another. If—a big if— suitable heliports were available in the heart of each city involved, the city-center to city-center type of operation could be very effective, New York Airways has demonstrated this with a twenty-five passenger, 140 miles-per-hour Boeing-Vertol 107 helicopter during trial runs between downtown New York and downtown Washington; the trip took only one hour and twenty minutes. The airlines of course can make it in less than an hour, and their fares are lower. But if you include the time and money spent on ground travel between the airport terminals and the downtown area—the helicopter (if downtown heliports were available) would go right to the heart of the city— the cost would be about the same and the copter would be faster.

Another factor in the over-all scheme of things is the technological development of new aircraft which should be more profitable to operate. Ten or fifteen years ago, when the copter lines began operating in major cities, they used a collection of various types of small aircraft just as the airlines did when they pioneered airplane service in the twenties and thirties. Eventually most of the helicopter lines (the ones that stayed in business) worked up to larger machines such as the Vertol Model 44, which could carry fifteen passengers at a cruising speed of nearly 100 miles per hour. Then, a few years ago (1962-1963), they graduated to what has been called the second generation of transport helicopters, the twin-engined turbine-powered types that include the Boeing-Vertol 107 and the Sikorsky S-61.

That these turbine helicopters (turbocopters) were a substantial improvement over the equipment that the lines had been using was demonstrated by the large increase in revenue miles flown by the lines in Los Angeles, Chicago, and New York during 1963; as a group they flew 12,510,000 revenue passenger miles, a rise of 52.7 per cent over the year before. Both the V-107 and the S-61 are capable of carrying over twenty-five passengers in the 140-mile-per-hour speed range. Another important feature of the turbocopters is that they are twin-engined, with the inherent safety factor of a reserve engine if one turbine should fail (as with a multi-engine airplane, the multi-engine helicopter is able to maintain flight under most conditions with only one engine functioning).

Unhappily, despite the gains from the introduction of the turbocopters, the helicopters are still in trouble financially.* The operating costs are simply too high, and this is reflected in high fares and low passenger volumes.

But the picture for the future is encouraging. It should be possible, the industry thinks, to have paying operations without government subsidies and with a fare low enough that passengers will find the service attractive. The approach is the same as that followed by the airlines in their long but successful search for the passenger dollar: larger, faster aircraft that can increase the number of paying passengers and number of trips that can be flown in any given time—in other words, more capacity and speed. The next generation of transport helicopters now under development are the fifty-seaters with speeds of 180 and 200 miles per hour. Furthermore, it is expected that these new aircraft will be better equipped for all-weather flight, thus decreasing the chances of cancellations due to bad weather.

To meet the problem satisfactorily, it has been estimated that this next generation of helicopters would have to have an operating cost as low as 7.7 cents per seat mile (one passenger seat flown a distance of one mile); this is the break-even point at which helicopter line operations would be economically feasible. By way of comparison, the cost per seat mile of the existing helicopter passenger operations now is two or three times this figure.

* With one significant exception—San Francisco and Oakland Helicopter Airlines—the helicopter carriers in the United States had depended heavily on government subsidies since the beginning of their operations. Constant Congressional attack finally ended the subsidy in 1965 (New York Airways received no federal funds after April 1965; support for Chicago Helicopter Airways and Los Angeles Airways ended on December 31 of the same year), and as a direct result, Chicago Helicopter Airways was forced to suspend operations after seventeen years of service. In the spring of 1966 the three survivors (NYA, LAA, and the never-subsidized SFOH as well) had to enter into various financial agreements with the trunk airlines that offered a chance for survival, at least for the time being.

Aside from the different transportation roles and the types of aircraft available, there is another key factor in the equation. One viewpoint has it that the ultimate success or failure of helicopter passenger service depends on the availability of heliports, particularly conveniently located rooftop heliports atop airline terminals or buildings.

There has been some opposition to rooftop heliports in city areas; one of the points constantly raised is the question of noise. But, says the industry, this is not supported by the facts. The large turbine-powered helicopters that have been in service for the last two or three years are quieter, if anything, than the smaller piston-engine aircraft which preceded them. Their engines work by turning drive-shafts that connect with the rotors: there is no outside jet blast, as with the turbojet engines that power large transport airplanes. Most of the noise, such as it is, comes from the sound of the whirling rotor blades slapping the air, not from the turbines. The noise levels from these large helicopters seems to be no more, if not less, than the noise from ordinary street traffic.

Another objection has been the possibility of accidents. It has been argued that helicopters operating in a city should use ground-level heliports facing on riverfronts to provide clear approach routes. Since most of the copters in scheduled passenger service today are amphibious, the open water around riverfront heliports does offer a major advantage in safety.

In rebuttal, proponents of the helicopter have some ready answers. They point to the marked improvement in reliability of the turbine engines, as compared to the piston engines used in the older ships. They emphasize the fact that with twin engines, a turbocopter can easily fly to an alternate landing spot if one engine should fail. They explain that approach and take-off routes have been planned so that, most of the time, even if the worst were to happen and both engines failed, the aircraft could easily glide (autorotate) to some safe, open spot such as a river. Concerning the problem of changing winds and air turbulence, the helicopter people say that careful choice of location and thorough testing (if necessary, special windshields or baffles could be built) eliminates this as a real hazard.

Perhaps the best argument of all is the hundreds of thousands, possibly millions, of safe landings and take-offs that have been made from rooftop heliports all over the world.

The industry feels that it is difficult to overemphasize the importance of convenient, strategically located heliports. In the last decade, helicopter men have had to relive the same kind of struggle which the airlines began over thirty years ago. Today, they are about where the airlines were ten or fifteen years ago: trying to make the big jump from depending on outside support to financial independence and a profitable future. They want to buy the new equipment which should help to take them out of the red and at the same time work to build good will and to attract as much business as possible. It is a crucial time. If the helicopter lines succeed in tapping the large and growing market of passengers through convenient, strategically placed heliports, more new equipment, and scheduling to suit the airlines, they have good reason to expect a bright future. Of the many factors involved, the question of well-placed heliports is particularly serious.

One influential advocate has been the *New York Times*. In an editorial published on July 9, 1963, the *Times* commented favorably, and in detail, on the heliport proposed for the top of the fifty-nine-story Pan American World Airways Building located in the center of the city:

> Such an operation from the heart of midtown Manhattan will mean a really significant relief from one of the major inconveniences of airplane travel—the time-consuming trip by congested highway to and from the airport. . . . The rooftop heliport is nothing new; it has been tested here and is in use in other cities. We believe that neighbors in the Pan Am area, a few of whom have been protesting while others welcome the new arrival, will not find the heliport objectionable on either noise or safety grounds. On the basis of scientific research, air-flow vanes have been installed to control turbulence on the heliport, and virtually all-weather operation is expected.

Both opponents and advocates of flight from city center rooftop heliports have overlooked one startling fact in the controversy over these high platforms for perching helicopters: the technique is anything but new. The first landings and take-offs by

70. *First copter to land on skyscraper in mid-town Manhattan, New York Airways V-107 approaches Pan American building heliport on May 23, 1964. This landing was preliminary to a formal test for city officials held a week later. Passenger service between the midtown heliport and Kennedy International Airport was inaugurated on December 22, 1965; by the end of March, 1966, New York Airways had carried over 45,000 passengers on the ten-minute flight to and from the airport. The number of passengers rose sharply during the thirteen-day transit strike in New York, with a record total for one day of almost 3,000 carried on January 5, 1966.*

71. *Eastern Air Lines pilot John M. Miller coolly leaps a Kellett KD-1 direct-control Autogiro from the roof of the Philadelphia Post Office Building on July 6, 1939, during the inauguration of a regular Autogiro mail service between Philadelphia and Camden. The single-seat KD-1 was powered by a 225-horsepower Jacobs engine and cruised at about 100 miles per hour, with a top speed of 125 and a range of 360 miles.*

rotating-wing aircraft from downtown rooftops took place before the helicopter itself was invented.

The older first cousin of the helicopter, the Autogiro, was flown from the rooftop of a Philadelphia post office as far back as 1935. On May 25 of that year, the first Autogiro airmail deliveries were made when a Pitcairn PA-22 and a Kellett KD-1 were both landed the same day during trials on the roof of the downtown Philadelphia Post Office. The mail flights were only demonstrations, not the start of regularly scheduled service. The Pitcairn machine was flown by the company's veteran Autogiro test pilot, Jim Ray. The Kellett was piloted by another pioneer, Lew Leavitt.

After four years, a scheduled full-time airmail service was inaugurated, by Eastern Air Lines, from the top of that same Philadelphia Post Office roof to nearby Camden Airport, six miles away. The service went on steadily for a year, with five round trips a day, and was finally discontinued because of the impending war emergency. The Kellett Autogiro used was much like the direct-control aircraft that had been demonstrated four years before; it was a KD-1 two-seater, modified into a single-seater with a mail compartment. Not the least surprising aspect of this giro airmail service was the "modern practical airport with complete two-way radiophone station" as Eastern Air Lines termed it, with "weather bureau, maintenance, and refueling facilities permanently installed." Since the Autogiros of that day could not hover in the air, they needed what was in effect a short runway to make a forward roll during landings and take-off.* Accordingly, the rooftop was "paved with asphalt and is underlined with steam pipes to melt snow and ice in winter." One interesting piece of equipment was the tiny fuel tank truck used for servicing the Autogiro with aviation gasoline, which rolled handily around the rooftop of the Post Office. To quote the airline's statement again, "The Gulf Oil Corporation built a replica of the company's large aviation gasoline trucks, in miniature, for servicing the Autogiro with aviation

* The KD-1 Autogiro was an advanced type capable of vertical take-off—it could "jump" straight up into the air for 30 or 40 feet before going into forward flight. But normally a running landing and take-off was preferred, since this was less of a strain on the engine; the same is true of helicopters today.

gasoline and oil on the roof." Today, one of the arguments against rooftop heliports is over the possible storage of fuel; even the relatively small amount of fuel in a helicopter's tanks is thought to be a possible hazard. It is surprising that apparently no objections were made in 1939 to a fuel truck servicing an aircraft on the roof of a public building. Instead, the autogiro service was received in all quarters with enthusiasm. Perhaps it was a simpler era, and people were less inclined to look for reasons why things should not be done.

VIII

Rotating Wings

"I had no need of sails to drive me, nor oars nor wheels to push me, nor rails to give me a faster road. Air is what I wanted, that was all. Air surrounds me as water surrounds the submarine boat, and in it my propellers act like the screws of a steamer. That is how I solved the problem of aviation. . . ."
—JULES VERNE in *Robur le conquerant* (1886)

THE MOTION of the blades of a helicopter in flight conjures up the ancient vision of the airscrew: lifting surfaces rotating about a vertical axis and inclined at an angle so, as they turn, a lifting force is obtained from the resistance of the air. This recurring theme in the history of aeronautics was crystallized in the writings of Leonardo Da Vinci. Centuries later, but still many years before the perfection of the helicopter, master storyteller Jules Verne wrote a novel *Robur le conquerant* in which his hero explained the functioning of the huge vertical take-off aircraft in which he cruises over the earth by comparing its propellers with the screws of a steamship.

Historically, much of the early helicopter experimentation developed from this concept of lifting surfaces operated as a kind of *airscrew*. Even today it is not too wide of the mark to use this term, especially if we take note of the screwlike spiral path made by the rotor blades when a helicopter rises straight up. But this is not the way it really works; for an understanding of what makes a helicopter fly it is necessary to take a different approach and consider the key phrase, "rotating-wing." For a helicopter flies as does an airplane, by the movement of its wings through the air. These wings, of course, are whirling rotor blades. This is the essence of helicopter flight—"wings" rotating around a central shaft.

A fuller understanding of rotating-wing aircraft really begins with the workings of the fixed-wing airplane. Here lies the similarity—and, paradoxically, the difference—between the two types of aircraft. In the most basic terms, a wing is a fixed surface that will produce a lifting force when it is moved through the air with enough speed or, as an engineer would put it, with sufficient velocity. To appreciate why a wing has this property, we need to consider the substance called air.

Air is a fluid that behaves just as do wet fluids such as water or oil. If you move through a fluid slowly it will resist—but give way—as the water in a swimming pool clings and then flows around you as you walk or swim through it. If you speed up your movement, the resistance (drag) will increase out of all proportion to the increase in speed. For example, if you move through it twice as fast as before, the drag will be four times as much. (An engineer would say that the resistance is going up by the *square* of the speed—multiplied by itself.) And consequently, this property has resulted in the art of streamlining, the creation of shapes that offer the least resistance so that movement through fluids can be accomplished with the least expenditure of power.

The trick in making a heavier-than-air machine fly is to take the resistance, which is trying to hold you back, and put it to work so that it provides a lifting force. As we saw in Chapter I, the means for accomplishing this was known for hundreds, even thousands of years before the first aircraft were flown. The lesson was learned from the ordinary kite: if a lightweight, flat surface was inclined at a slight angle to a constant airflow (the wind), a lifting force resulted and the surface rose and flew. In more precise aeronautical terminology, the front or *leading edge* of the lifting surface had to be raised higher, relative to the air flowing against it, than the rear edge.

In the same way, a lifting force results as air is pushed down by the slanting undersurface of a wing or rotor blade. The faster the movement through the air, the stronger the reaction and the greater the lifting force. What is happening is that the surface is being supported by "planing", sliding along on a mass of piled-up fluid. The name that has been accepted for the fixed-wing flying machine, "airplane," is in itself a substantial clue to the workings of a wing in flight. One way actually to feel this lifting force is to hold your hand stiffly, at a slight angle, in a steady blast of air.

The kite, so much a classic example of why an airplane flies that at least one aeronautical authority refers to all airplanes as basically "kitecraft," is still useful today for illustrating this principle of flight. When held at the correct *angle of attack* to the wind by the balance between its rag tail and the kite string, it will maintain itself steadily in the air; it is a lifting surface that is supported by the pressure of the stream of air. This stream is the *relative airflow*—that is, a flow of air relative to the inclined angle of the lifting surface. This flow can be created by holding the surface still in a moving airflow, or the air can be at rest with the lifting surface being moved through it rapidly, as with the wing of an airplane or the rotor blades of a helicopter. In both cases the effect is exactly the same: a constant airflow against a lifting surface. For example, a kite that was being pulled along at a steady 10 miles an hour in still air would be lifting in exactly the same manner, with the same force, as a kite riding in a constant 10-mile-an-hour wind.

If we were to install an engine and propeller on our kite, and tail surfaces to balance it and hold the right angle of attack, it could be made to create its own relative airflow simply by moving through the air. Of course, the self-propelled kite* that we have imagined here is actually an airplane, basically nothing more than a powered kite that planes through the air, and the transition we have made here from kite to free-flying aircraft

---

* If the same imaginary kite were set at the correct angle of attack and rotated on an arm around a shaft it would, of course, produce a lifting force; in effect it would be a rotating wing, the essence of the helicopter.

actually parallels the historical development of the airplane; before they flew the world's first powered plane at Kitty Hawk in 1903 the Wright brothers spent years testing man-carrying kites.

Yet, though the term "planing" is helpful in creating a visual image of the action of a lifting surface, it must be said that this does nothing to explain how the actual lift forces are produced or show the real effect on the air mass. The theoretical aspects cannot be adequately explained here; however, several important points are plain enough and can be described. One concept is that the moving wing creates a *vortex system* (air moving in a circular pattern) which deflects the air downward.

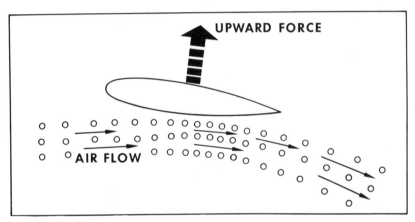

72. *An illustration of the force produced by an airfoil operating at a positive angle of attack to an airflow; normally this force is inclined upward and slightly to the rear. The airfoil shown here is symmetrical: the curves on the upper and lower surfaces are identical.*

This in turn produces a reaction on the wing in the opposite direction, the lift force that supports the aircraft. A useful and interesting description of the ultimate effect, not only on the air mass but on the earth below as well, is furnished in a U.S. Air Force textbook, *Foundations of Airpower*. It is quoted in part as follows:

> The wing produces lift by driving air downward. The more rapidly and efficiently it does this, the more lift it will produce. A

wing is therefore the same, in this respect at least, as a helicopter rotor, a ducted fan, or other lift-creating devices.

But it is not the air that ultimately supports the airplane.

Consider a tub of water weighing 50 pounds. If you float a 5-pound toy boat in it, the combination must weigh 55 pounds. The boat does not cease to have weight merely because it is floating; its weight, too, must be supported by the scale.

Ultimately it is the earth that provides the reaction upward against the air directly beneath the aircraft. The air merely transmits the weight of the aircraft down to the ground. But since the air pressures decrease with the square of the height of the aircraft, they are extremely small by the time they reach any particular point on the ground (unless the plane is only a few feet* up).

There are other factors that are also at work in the creation of lift by an airfoil. One that is frequently mentioned in older textbooks is the "Bernoulli effect," which relates to the flow of air over the upper surface of the wing as well as against the lower surface. Basically, this theory says that because of the angle of attack at which the airflow strikes the leading edge (and also because of the thick curve found on the upper surface of many airfoils), the air traveling over the top of the wing is forced to travel a greater distance than the air going under the bottom. In order to avoid creating a vacuum behind the trailing edge, the theory says, the airflow over the top has to speed up to a velocity greater than that of the flow on the bottom. This difference in velocity is the key to the lifting effect; the theorem expounded by the eighteenth-century scientist Daniel Bernoulli states that as the velocity of the airflow over a surface *increases,* the direct atmospheric pressure on the surface *decreases.* Therefore, the difference in the speed of the flow between the upper and lower surfaces causes a difference in atmospheric pressure; specifically, there is more pressure on the lower surface of the wing than on the upper, and a lifting force results.

Interestingly, the vortex or circulation theory that we mentioned earlier is frequently considered to be an extension of

---

* An airplane flying just a few feet from the ground derives added lift from this pressure; this is actually another manifestation of the ground effect that benefits a helicopter when it is hovering close to the earth.

the Bernoulli theorem. Without getting the reader too involved in, and confused with, the theory of lift it must be said that both of the explanations provided here (there are still more) are really oversimplifications of a very complex airflow system and do not correspond with all of the realities of the situation.

In any case, to move on to a safer subject, the effectiveness of a lifting surface depends greatly on the shape of its airfoil; this is the shape that you would see if you could imagine slicing across a wing or a rotor blade from the leading to the trailing edge, at right angles to the span. It can be thought of as two curves, the one on the top surface and the one on the bottom, joined together to form a streamlined shape. With many of the older standard airfoils this takes the form of a kind of arched-out teardrop curve on top that goes down to a knife edge at the rear, combined with a bottom surface that is nearly flat.

Basically, the airfoil shape serves two closely interrelated functions. The first, obviously, is to obtain the maximum lifting force. Secondly, the shape of the airfoil is intended to permit the wing to move through the air with as little resistance as possible: it is the best shape for the work it has to do. In the language of the aeronautical engineer the efficiency of an airfoil, with regard to these two functions, is expressed in terms of the "lift-drag ratio." An airfoil with the best lift-drag ratio for a particular aircraft is simply the one that furnishes the greatest lift with the least resistance (drag) to the airflow.

Surprisingly, this very special airfoil shape, as well as many of the other aerodynamic shapes used in aircraft design, have frequently been determined more by trial and error than anything else. This helps to explain why elaborate wind tunnels and extremely accurate scale models are so important to aerodynamic research. Obviously, if it is necessary to test endless combinations of shapes and curves you must have some way to duplicate the interaction between the airflow and the shape without building a whole new wing or rotor for every experiment.

One type has exactly the same amount of curvature on the bottom as on the top: this is often referred to as a "symmetrical"

*73. The drawing opposite shows the main parts of an Alouette heli-
copter. Produced in France by Sud-Aviation since 1953 and used
widely throughout the world, the general-purpose Alouette was one
of the first to be powered with a turboshaft engine. Several different
versions have been built; the model in the drawing is the Alouette-
Astazou, equipped with a Turbomeca Astazou engine of 360 shaft
horsepower. The large fuel tank (boxlike structure behind cabin),
compared to the small size of the engine, is typical of turbine-
powered aircraft.*

airfoil. Many helicopter rotor blades have this shape — a
stretched-out teardrop curve from the leading edge to the trailing edge that is exactly the same on both the top and the bottom.
In comparison with the more conventionally shaped airfoils the
symmetrical airfoil offers several advantages, particularly for
the rotor blades of a helicopter. One of the most important of
these is a highly desirable aerodynamic characteristic: very
little center-of-pressure change under different angles of attack
(the center of pressure is generally considered to be the center
of the lift force acting on the wing).* (With conventional
airfoils that have a full curve only on top, as the angle of attack
is increased the center of pressure moves forward considerably,
and this complicates the problem of stabilizing and controlling
the lifting surface.) Other desirable features of a rotor blade
designed with a symmetrical airfoil are structural rather than
aerodynamic. For one thing they are generally easier to manufacture, since the top and bottom skins are identical and other
parts may be as well.

Up to this point our discussion has centered on theory of lift
and the shape of airfoils best suited to the rotating wings of a
helicopter. The second phase of this chapter will deal with the
functioning of the flight controls. In a sense, dividing the
subject into these two categories parallels the development of
the helicopter. The first phase, roughly up until the early
1920's, dealt largely with the problem of perfecting rotors that

* Obviously, lift is generated over the entire surface of the wing. However,
for theoretical purposes this force is considered to be centered at one point—
this is the *center of pressure*, in effect the balancing point for the entire lift
force.

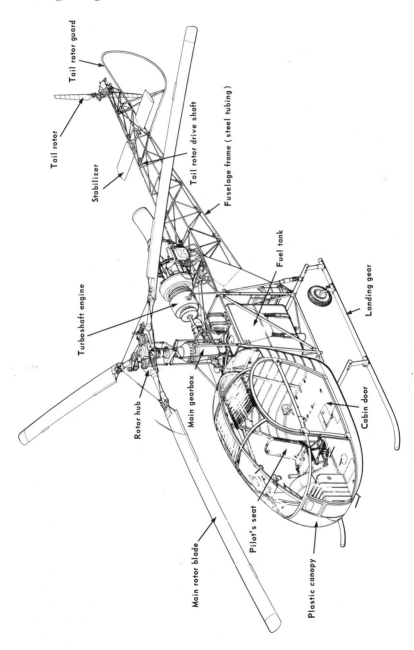

Tail rotor guard

Tail rotor

Stabilizer

Tail rotor drive shaft

Fuselage frame (steel tubing)

Fuel tank

Landing gear

Turboshaft engine

Cabin door

Rotor hub

Main gearbox

Main rotor blade

Pilot's seat

Plastic canopy

were efficient enough to permit flight. The next step, through the 1930's and into the 1940's, was the perfection of control systems and mechanisms that would provide the capability for real flight at a fair rate of speed.

. Our examination of the pilot's control system will be limited to one helicopter configuration, surely the best example, the type which incorporates one main overhead rotor with a small tail rotor at the rear of the fuselage. This classic form, perfected by Igor I. Sikorsky in the United States between 1939 and 1941, remains the predominant type today, although there have been many successful aircraft with various other rotor configurations; these are described in Chapter III. It should be noted that the control systems described here are not limited to the single main rotor type but are employed in one form or another in most helicopters, no matter what the rotor configuration.

With the Sikorsky configuration, the small tail rotor is intended to offset the torque reaction mentioned in earlier chapters. Torque has no effect while the aircraft is sitting on the ground, since the ship is prevented from rotating by the weight on the landing gear. But once the ship is clear of the ground, the torque effect tries to take over. The practical effect of this—as far as the pilot is concerned—is simply that the tail has a tendency to swing in one direction. To prevent this, a small anti-torque rotor is mounted at the tail, driven by an extension shaft from the engine transmission. This tail rotor is really more like an airplane propeller, since it turns much faster than the main rotor. To keep the helicopter moving straight ahead without turning, the pitch of the tail rotor blades must be just enough exactly to counteract the force of the torque reaction. On most helicopters with a single main rotor, the pitch of the tail rotor is adjusted so that at cruise speed the aircraft is trimmed to fly a straight course.

Besides holding the tail end of the fuselage straight against the twisting force of torque, this rear rotor provides control for steering to the right or left, as does the rudder of an airplane. This is accomplished by the pilot's *foot pedals*, which control the pitch angle of the tail rotor blades: by pressing on the right pedal, the pitch is decreased and the tail swings to the left.

Pressing on the left pedal, of course, has the opposite effect: the pitch of the tail rotor is increased so that its thrust now overcomes the torque and tail swings the other way.

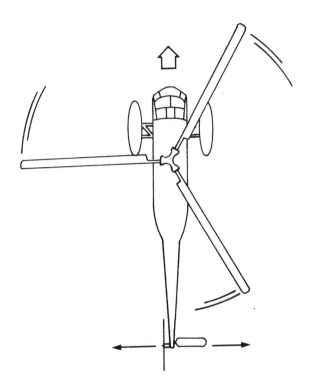

74. The small tail rotor of a helicopter controls the heading of the aircraft by turning the fuselage to the right or left. This is accomplished by the pilot through the movement of foot pedals linked to the tail rotor pitch control, so that by increasing or decreasing pitch he is able to swing the tail to either side. The tail rotor also serves to counteract the torque reaction of the main rotor.

The term "control is yaw" is used to describe this effect of the tail rotor—that is, the ability to swing the tail to the right or to the left. Unlike the rudder of an airplane, it isn't necessary for the helicopter to be in forward motion in order for the tail rotor to be effective; as long as the main rotor is turning over the tail rotor will keep spinning, owing to the mechanical drive

75. *A close-up view of the cockpit of the Hughes Model 269A shows both seats and dual flight controls. A cyclic control stick, similar to an airplane stick, is located in front of each seat. The collective pitch lever is between the two seats; moving it up or down increases or decreases the pitch angle of all three rotor blades simultaneously. A twist-type throttle for the engine is mounted on the collective lever. All flight controls are shown except the rudder pedals, located on the floor in front of each seat. The 269A, a light two-seater, is one of the smallest helicopters in service.*

system that links them together, and the tail control will continue to function. This feature is important in the event of an engine failure or if the engine is slowed deliberately. In this situation the helicopter descends with the main rotor freewheeling in autorotation. The fact that the tail rotor will keep turning with the power cut off means that directional (yawing) conrol can be maintained, and the pilot will still be able to steer the aircraft as it descends.

Another primary control used to fly a helicopter is the *collective pitch stick,* located to the left of the pilot's seat and mounted on a pivot so the pilot can ease it up and down with his left hand. By means of this control the pilot can increase or decrease the pitch angle of all the blades in the main rotor, equally and simultaneously. For example, to make the aircraft rise, he pulls up on the collective stick—this is called *"pulling in pitch"*—and the effect is to increase the pitch angle of the blades and thus, to increase the lift. However, as the blades meet the air at a greater angle of attack,* the drag on the rotor will increase as well as the lift. Therefore, to maintain a constant rotational speed it is necessary to increase the power by speeding up the engine as the stick is raised.

This brings us to yet another control, the *throttle* for the engine. Since the pilot already has both hands and feet occupied, the problem is solved by providing a rotating handle (similar to the twist grip found on a motorcycle) mounted directly on the collective stick. As the pilot pulls in pitch by raising the stick with his left hand he also twists the throttle slightly to speed up the engine.

* A fuller explanation of the terms "pitch angle" and "angle of attack," as they apply to an airfoil, is furnished in the Appendix.

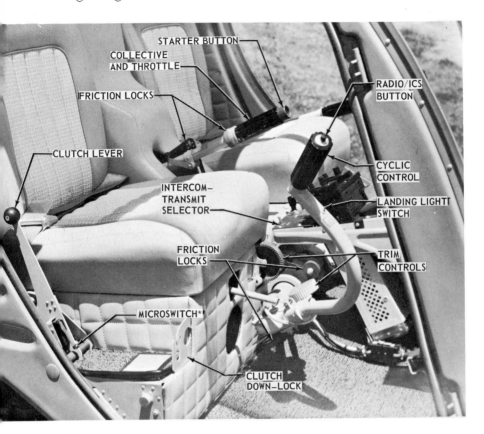

We can see how this control is used by following the actual motions that the pilot makes during take-off. First, he will bring the rotor up to the correct speed by opening the twist-grip throttle. He then eases up on the collective pitch stick, increasing the bite of the main blades while simultaneously adjusting the power of the engine to maintain the rotor speed. When the lift force developed by the rotor becomes greater than the weight of the aircraft, the landing gear will begin to clear the ground. In a condition of hovering flight the lift exactly equals the weight, and the pilot can then raise or lower the helicopter by increasing or decreasing his collective pitch.

The technique of using the left hand to operate both the throttle and the collective stick is one of the problems peculiar to flying a helicopter. Coordination of the throttle and the collective pitch is vital in maintaining the speed of the rotor at the all-important correct number of revolutions per minute. To make the task easier for the pilot, most of today's helicopters employ a mechanical linkage in the collective control which automatically adds throttle as the pitch is increased. However, with many helicopters the pilot still has the chore of making

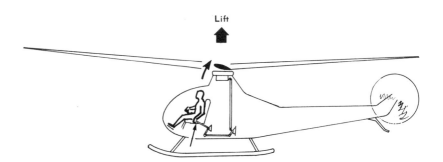

76. To rise vertically, the pilot raises the collective pitch stick with his left hand. This increases the pitch angle of all rotor blades simultaneously, thus increasing the over-all lift.

constant small corrections in spite of the action of this linkage.

The last primary flight control is the cyclic control stick. The cyclic stick is mounted vertically from the cockpit floor, between the pilot's legs, in the same position as the control stick of an airplane, which it so greatly resembles. Like the control stick of an airplane, it can be moved slightly in any direction

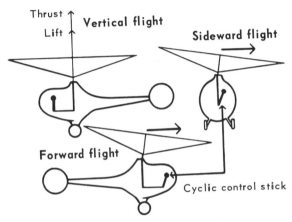

77. *These three illustrations show the effect of the pilot's cyclic control stick; the direction of flight follows the direction in which the stick is moved. When the stick is moved to the front or rear, or to either side, the "disc of rotation" is inclined in that direction.*

from the vertical. With this control the pilot can move the helicopter in any direction horizontally—that is, for flying straight ahead, backing up, and for moving to either side.

When the cyclic stick is moved fore or aft, to either side, or in any combination of these, the whole whirling rotor system—termed the "disc of rotation"—will be tilted in the same direction and the movement of the helicopter will be in this direction. This is accomplished by changing the pitch angle—and thus the angle of attack—of each blade in cycles, from a maximum to a minimum position, as the blade sweeps through a complete revolution. The way this works is illustrated by what happens when the rotor disc is tilted forward, to move the helicopter into forward flight. The pilot pushes his control stick forward slightly; the result is that the blade which happens to be at the rear of the disc has its pitch increased by the control linkage, while the blade which happens to be moving around at the front has its pitch decreased. Since each blade is attached to the hub by a hinge which allows it to flap up and down slightly as it turns (here we are describing a standard articulated rotor), the blade at the rear will rise upward and then, as it moves around to the front, it will ride at a lower than normal position. The over-all effect is that the rotor disc— actually the path the blades take describes the shape of a shallow cone rather than a disc—will be inclined forward so that its lift is no longer straight up but is now pulling slightly forward as well. In the same way, the cyclic stick can be used to incline the rotor to move the helicopter in other directions.

An important function of the cyclic control system is that it allows the pilot to correct for *dissymmetry of lift*. This phenomenon was mentioned in Chapter II, which dealt with the development of the Autogiro; it refers to the unequal lifting forces created as the helicopter speeds up and moves forward through the air that, unless corrected, can cause the aircraft to roll to one side. To understand this, it is helpful to visualize the position of each blade in relation to the airflow coming from the front as it sweeps through the full 360-degree circle of rotation. Each blade can be thought of as advancing when it sweeps forward against the airflow from the front, and retreating when it swings past the straight-ahead position and begins to move to the rear on the other side of the circle. Since the blades obtain lift from both the airflow induced by their rotation and from the flow from the front, it is not surprising that the advancing blade, which is meeting the flow from the front head on, will create more lift than the retreating blade. Because of this, the advancing blade will tend to flap up while the retreating blade, which is "running away" from the airflow from the front, will flap down. The effect is that the rising blade is actually decreasing its angle of attack, since the movement of the air against the blade is no longer horizontal but is now slightly *downward*—owing to the blade moving *upward*. On the other side of the rotor the situation is reversed; there the blade is actually increasing its angle of attack since it is "diving down" against the airflow. This flapping effect is quite beneficial because it results in an equalization of the angle of attack—and therefore the lift force—created on the right and left sides of the rotor disc, and eliminates the tendency for the helicopter to roll to one side.

However, there is an undesirable result from this flapping action which can be overcome through use of the cyclic pitch control. As the advancing blade flaps upward it reaches its highest flapped position directly in front, one-quarter of a revolution from the point where the increased lift began to take effect. Conversely, the retreating blade reaches its lowest flapped position directly to the rear, over the tail of the helicopter. Therefore the tendency of the aircraft to roll, eliminated by the flapping of the blades, is now changed to a tendency for the rotor disc to pitch to the rear and thus for the helicopter to climb as it goes into forward flight. This might seem to call for still more complications in the control system, but fortunately this is not the case. To start the ship moving forward initially, the pilot had pushed his cyclic stick forward. To overcome the climbing tendency he simply pushes the stick still farther forward, responding naturally to the nose-up position, and the rotor disc remains in the desired attitude.

One of the important characteristics of lift dissymmetry is that it becomes much worse as the helicopter speeds up and flies faster. Since the lift on the blades on the advancing side cannot be permitted to exceed the lift on the retreating side, this factor tends to limit the top speed at which the fastest helicopters (with conventional rotor systems) can fly; for even the largest and most powerfully-engined of helicopters, at speeds just above 200 miles per hour the lifting and propelling characteristics of the rotor are affected, and a phenomenon termed "blade stall" is encountered.*

With these primary controls—pedals for steering, the collective pitch stick (with the twist throttle), and the cyclic stick—the pilot can move his ship in any direction, turning it around on the axis of the main rotor, moving it up, down,

---

* A more detailed explanation of blade stall is provided in the Appendix.

forward, to the rear, and sideways. Obviously, a helicopter pilot can be very busy indeed. Each hand and both feet may be at work at the same time, and the pilot's left hand will have two jobs to do simultaneously, pulling up on the pitch stick while feeding in power with the throttle. Added to this is the fact that most copters do not possess the inherent stability found in airplanes, being in this respect more comparable to an automobile than an airplane; you can't let go of the controls for more than a few seconds at a time. But these seemingly complicated motions are easily absorbed, and a natural pattern of action and reaction is quickly established by most student pilots.

Thus far, we have been concerned primarily with the helicopter's flight while the rotor is under power, being driven around by the engine. However there is another condition of flight, autorotation, when the blades will continue to turn and produce lift even though the power has been reduced or stopped entirely. In autorotation the helicopter is descending with the airflow coming up through the rotor from the front and below, rather than from above as happens in normal powered flight. This characteristic can hardly be overestimated since it provides an important safety factor. If the engine should fail the helicopter can still descend safely—provided the pilot handles the controls correctly and quickly lowers his collective stick to the low pitch angle required for the blades to autorotate. (The autorotational descent of a helicopter has been compared to the glide of an airplane with a dead engine.) In autorotation the airflow meets the rotor blades at angle of attack which induces a lift force inclined slightly forward, so that it serves to pull the blades around and thus keeps the rotor turning.

To permit the autorotational forces to do their work in an emergency, it is necessary to design various mechanisms into the power drive system to the rotor. These are freewheeling systems which ensure that the rotor can keep turning freely if the engine stops, or even if the transmission or some other part were to jam. On most helicopters there is not just one system but three or more, each functioning independently, to guarantee that the blades will continue to rotate.

Of the instruments installed in the cockpit, one in particular is worth describing because it is unique to the helicopter and is important for the pilot's control of rotor speed. This is the *rotor tachometer*, the instrument that indicates the number of revolutions per minute. In an airplane this instrument shows the revolutions of the engine alone. But in a helicopter, this one instrument provides the revolutions per minute of both the engine and the rotor on one clock face. This is accomplished by having two pointers, or needles, superimposed on the same shaft. One needle points to an inner scale on the face of the instrument with one set of values while the other needle points to an outer scale with a different set of numbers; one needle indicates the rotor revolutions, the other shows the revolutions of the engine.* In normal flight these two pointers will ordinarily remain together, since an increase in engine revolutions will of course result in a speeding up of the rotor. However, if engine power is suddenly reduced, as when the pilot chops back the throttle to go into an autorotational glide, the engine needle will fall away from the rotor needle since the rotor tends to maintain its speed—at first because of the inertia of the rotating mass, and then because of the aerodynamic force of autorotation. This is termed "splitting the needles."

* For example, the rotor speed of the small three-place Hughes Model 200 helicopter during cruise is approximately 450 revolutions per minute, while the engine speed is approximately 2,800 revolutions.

IX

The Rotor Mechanism

"The history of the helicopter is filled with attempts to reduce complication . . . invariably this turns into a game of Chinese checkers as the designer feverishly moves the complicated problem from one part to another, never getting rid of it."
—D. H. KAPLAN, designer of the Quadrotor (1956)

JUAN DE LA CIERVA was unimpressed with the helicopter approach to flight, writing, in 1931, "there is no such thing as a simple helicopter as a practical flying machine." This was a fair enough statement for 1931, and if the word "simple" is kept in mind it is still true today. Yet, ironically, in a few years his creation was instrumental in the perfection of the helicopter. Although they could not hover or climb to any great height vertically, Cierva's rotorplanes were eminently successful and added new links in the chain of rotating-wing knowledge. Without the Autogiro people being entirely aware of it, their machines were serving as flying test-beds for systems that would eventually be used in helicopters.

One example was in the design of rotor blades. The Autogiro's blades had evolved into long slender units with a good airfoil shape—true rotating wings, as opposed to the primitive, fan-shaped "airscrew" rotors found on many early helicopters. The lengthy blades of the Autogiro turned through a greater circle than the stubby short-span rotors then being tried for

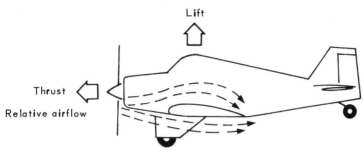

Airplane

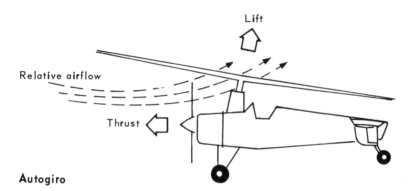

Autogiro

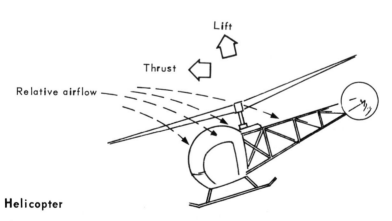

Helicopter

78. *The airflow patterns created by the forward flight of an airplane, an Autogiro, and a helicopter are compared here. With the Autogiro, the rotor mast is inclined to the rear and the airflow into the rotor is from the front and below. In the helicopter, the rotor is inclined forward and the flow enters from above.*

helicopters, thus providing that much more disc area to support the weight of the aircraft. An aeronautical engineer would describe this advantage as a "lower disc loading" (less weight for each square foot of disc area), and eventually helicopter experimenters followed this lead.

Another basic improvement, stemming from Cierva's work and perhaps even more important than the shape of the blades, was the system for hinging each blade to the hub. This arrangement, described in some detail in Chapters II and VIII, permitted each blade to flap and to adjust to the unequal lift forces created on opposite sides of the rotor disc as the aircraft sped into forward flight.

There were other important benefits gained from experience with the Autogiro. The use of autorotation itself to turn an unpowered rotor pointed the way to a means of making a safe power-off landing in a helicopter. The late-model direct-control and jump-take-off giros of the 1930's went even further: improved systems of control to the rotor head, methods for making pitch changes to the blades, mechanical drive systems— all were developed, and frequently by trial and error. Not that current methods are so very different. It is probably more true of helicopter design than any other phase of aerospace engineering that the personal element still enters into the equation. The creative process of designing a successful helicopter— particularly the rotor system—to this day has something in common with the free-for-all experimentation of the aeronautical pioneers.

Although designers have created an impressive number of rotor systems, it is possible to narrow the field down to three basic types: articulated, semi-rigid, and rigid rotors. There are rotor systems that seem to fall outside this threefold classification, but for the most part these are only variations or combinations of the three types. In this connection, it should be appreciated that the term "rotor" or "rotor system" refers to a single unit only, composed of just one hub and the blades attached to it. A helicopter may have more than one main rotor; multiple arrangements of two, three, four or even more rotors have been found on various aircraft at different times in history, but each rotor is considered a separate system. For the purposes of the explanations that follow (which deal primarily with the various types of rotor hubs and the workings of cyclic pitch control) we will be concerned primarily with the most widely used type, the Sikorsky configuration, which has just one main rotor, in combination with a small tail rotor.

The most important part of the system is the hub at the center. Here are concentrated all the forces generated by the movement of the blades through the air; aerodynamic, centrifugal, and inertia factors are involved that create very great loads which simultaneously pull the blades upward and outward. The hub is designed, for the most part, to accommodate and control these forces automatically, and the working of its mechanism is the very essence of the helicopter's mechanical nature. In dealing with the three basic types of rotor systems we will describe how some of these forces affect the rotor hub.

The *articulated rotor* system is the oldest; it appeared on the Autogiros of the 1920's and was incorporated in the first work-

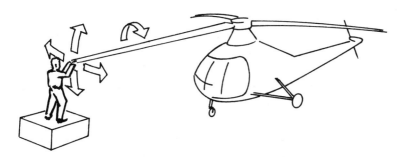

79. In a helicopter with an articulated rotor system, there are three kinds of movement for the rotor blade as it turns around the mast: up and down (flapping), back and forth in the horizontal plane (lead and lag), and changes in the pitch angle.

able helicopters of the 1930's. (The Autogiro ancestry of the articulated rotor prompted an earlier name, the "Cierva rotor.") Today it is perhaps still the most widely used type, in one form or another.

In this system, exclusive of the rotation of the blades about the mast, each individual blade is attached so that it can move in three different ways about the hub. One movement is common to almost all helicopters and types of rotor systems: the turning of the blades along their span-wise axis, owing to the action of the pilot's controls, in order to change the pitch angle. The other two kinds of motion, however, are not under the pilot's immediate control. These are movements the blades make in response to the powerful natural forces acting on the rotor, for which the articulated hub provides the necessary mechanisms—specifically, hinges—which permit freedom of movement so the blades can "articulate," or flap up and down and move back and forth slightly in the horizontal plane. The pivot which permits the up-and-down movement is usually called the "flapping" hinge, while the fore-and-aft pivot, mounted vertically, which allows the blade to move back and forth slightly in the horizontal plane, is called the "drag" hinge.

The flapping hinge provides the blades with flapping freedom, which permits each blade to rise and fall, as it turns, so the tip rides higher or lower in its circular path. While the hinge may be located very close to the center of the rotor drive shaft, it is more frequently designed to be a short distance from this center line. This is termed an "offset" flapping hinge, and it offers the designer a number of important advantages. The flapping motion is the result of the constantly changing balance between lift, centrifugal, and inertial forces; this rising and falling of the blades is characteristic of most helicopters and has often been compared to the beating of a bird's wing. (In Chapter VIII we described the way the pilot's cyclic pitch control utilizes blade flapping to incline the rotor disc and how the rising and falling of the blades helps to overcome lift dissymmetry when the helicopter is in forward flight.) One other point should be mentioned; the flapping hinge, in company with the natural flexibility found in most blades, permits

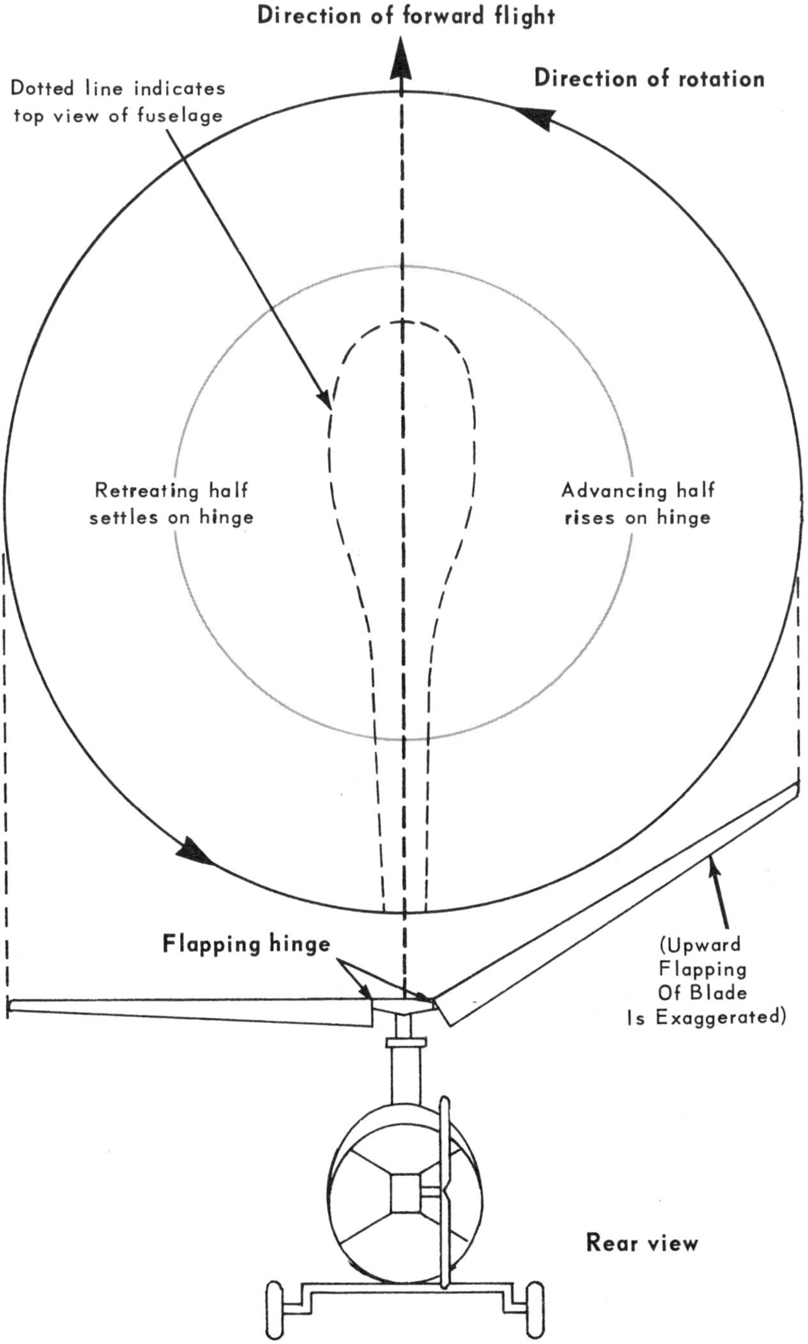

Direction of forward flight

Direction of rotation

Dotted line indicates
top view of fuselage

Retreating half
settles on hinge

Advancing half
rises on hinge

Flapping hinge

(Upward
Flapping
Of Blade
Is Exaggerated)

Rear view

80. *Flapping hinges in the rotor hub help to adjust the unequal lift forces in the right and left halves of the rotor's circle as the helicopter moves through the air in forward flight. The hinges permit the blades to rise and fall as they turn, thus varying the angle of attack so as to equalize the lift forces.*

the blade to droop considerably when the helicopter is at rest
and the rotor is not turning over. During flight the necessary
rigidity is provided by the powerful centrifugal force which
results from the rotation of the blades; this force pulls outward
from the tip, stiffening the blade, and is actually the only
factor which keeps it from folding up.*

The vertically mounted drag hinge as we have already noted,
permits each blade to move back and forth slightly in the
horizontal plane independently of the movement of the other

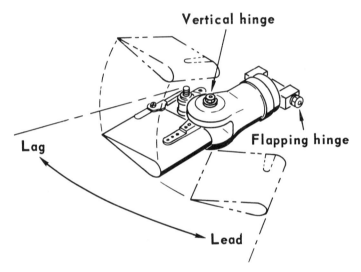

*81. Drawing shows root attachment of rotor blade to an articulated
hub. The flapping hinge permits each blade to rise and fall as it turns,
and the vertically mounted drag hinge allows lead-lag motion.*

blades. The terms "dragging," "hunting," and "lead-lag" are
also used to describe this movement, which is necessary to
relieve the powerful forces that might otherwise bend and even
break the blades. To prevent this back-and-forth hunting from
developing into serious vibration, it is restricted by hydraulic
dampers which slow down and "damp" the movement; this
action is very similar to the damping effect of an ordinary
hydraulic door-closer. The early Autogiros, incidentally, used
friction discs to accomplish the same thing.

* This is described in greater detail in the Appendix under "Rotor Decay."

The position that the blades actually assume while the helicopter is in flight obviously is the result of the various forces acting upon them. Normally, the blades will be lagged back slightly on the drag hinge and tilted up a few degrees on the flapping hinge; this upward tilt is termed the "coning angle" and is the result of the lifting force pulling upward on each blade while, simultaneously, centrifugal force is pulling outward. Since the centrifugal loading is so much greater, the blades only tilt upward a few degrees, and their path through the air takes the form of a shallow cone.

The articulated type of rotor is designed to leave the blades as free as possible, to avoid trying to restrict their natural tendencies to flap up and down or move in the horizontal plane. One effect is that the blades can be very slender and light, since great strength is required only to resist the tension of the powerful centrifugal force pulling along the span of the blade. An articulated blade is designed to have the inertial, centrifugal, and aerodynamic forces developed in flight all balancing about the same point on the blade chord—this is ordinarily one-fourth of the way back from the leading edge, or, as it is called, the "quarter chord point." Balancing the forces in this manner makes it possible for the pilot to control the blades with a minimum of effort and tends to hold down vibration as well. These highly desirable characteristics are reasons why the traditional articulated rotor is still so widely used.

The other two types of rotors are the semi-rigid and the rigid (or "hingeless"). Both are primary types currently in use, and both duplicate the function of the articulated rotor. Though different mechanisms are involved, the aerodynamic effects are essentially the same.

In the *semi-rigid rotor* (sometimes called a "rocking hub" or "teetering" rotor), the blades are attached rigidly to the hub but the hub itself is free to tilt in any direction about the top of the mast. Although there is no lead-lag movement, the blades can still flap or, in the true sense, rock up and down in order to compensate for dissymmetry of lift when moving forward. Semi-rigid rotors have appeared on helicopters with two, three, and four blades and provide some simplification, although they cause other problems. One important advantage is the fact that there are no drag hinges, and therefore no drag dampers are required. But there are complications including the necessity for providing a type of universal joint between the drive shaft and the rotor hub.

The *rigid rotor*, which until fairly recently was still in the experimental stage, is used in relatively few helicopters. In theory the rigid rotor is similar to an ordinary propeller; the blades are fixed to the hub without hinges and the hub in turn is fixed to the shaft.* Of the various systems, it is closest to the elemental concept of the airscrew which tantalized experimenters in centuries past. (Obviously, there can be no such thing as a completely rigid rotor, since all blades inherently exhibit some degree of flexibility—from a structural viewpoint it would be almost impossible to build a truly rigid blade.) Since there are no flapping hinges, or any other provisions for movement at the hub, other systems have been developed to overcome the unequal forces on the rotor, including pre-coning and feathering of the blades.

Pre-coning, as the word suggests, is an arrangement for pre-setting the blade at a slight upward angle from the hub to the tip. This is the same angle that the blade would ordinarily take, due to its coning upward in normal flight. If the upward tilt for average operating conditions is determined, and the blades mounted on the hub at this angle, the bending loads can be reduced materially. Pre-coning is thus a fairly simple design approach for dealing with the stresses on a semi-rigid or rigid rotor.

Feathering, on the other hand, involves the incorporation of an entirely new mechanism in the rotor head. This system compensates for the lift differential between the advancing and retreating blades by reducing the angle of attack as the blade starts to rise and decreasing it as the blade starts to fall; this, of course, means that the blade has to be mounted on the

---

* The term "rigid rotor" can be used to describe any rotor system that does not specifically provide flapping and dragging hinges.

hub, so that it can be rotated along its span-wise axis. As part of the system, the hub mechanism can be designed so the pitch changes are made automatically by the flapping (in this case the term "coning" is sometimes used, as well) of the blades as they turn. As the blade starts to flap, it activates linkage which changes the blade's angle of attack. This technique has been incorporated in many modern helicopters; the arrangement has been called "pitch-cone coupling."

The semirigid and rigid rotor systems represent attempts to simplify helicopter design, but the end result more often than not has usually been the need for added complications such as pre-coning or pitch-cone coupling, which tend to defeat the designer's original aim. This pattern has been repeated over and over again in the development of new rotor systems and of other parts of the helicopter, as well; the designer succeeds in simplifying one mechanism and finds that he has to add another device somewhere else in the system.

The problem of trying to reduce complexities that refuse to be banished has plagued designers since the days of the first helicopters. One experimenter, D. H. Kaplan (designer of the Quadrotor mentioned in Chapter III), in writing of the intricacies of the rotor cyclic control system, summed up one part of the puzzle thus: "In a cyclic-controlled rotor, every time the designer tries to deny the blade a freedom, it demands compensation somewhere else in the rotor mechanism. The history of the helicopter is filled with attempts to reduce complication . . . invariably this turns into a game of Chinese checkers as the designer feverishly moves the complicated problem from one part to another, never getting rid of it."

As with the other mechanisms found on a modern helicopter, the rudiments of the cyclic system can be traced back to the Autogiro, on which the first effective rotating-wing controls were developed. The designers of the first Autogiros of the early 1920's did not attempt to control the rotor blades directly. Instead, conventional airplane-type controls were furnished—rudder, elevators, ailerons mounted on stub wings—and the rotor was controlled by the aerodynamic forces on these surfaces, as was described in Chapter II.

Since the ailerons were outside the propeller slipstream (the direct blast of air from the propeller), at low airspeeds they were the weakest link in the system; eventually a method was devised for obtaining lateral control by "rocking" the rotor hub from side to side. This meant that the ailerons and the stub wings that supported them could be dispensed with, and the wingless Autogiro appeared.

The rocking head played a part in the development of cyclic pitch control systems. When the system was applied to some of the early helicopters, it was used for rocking the head not only from side to side but in all directions; in effect the hub was now mounted on a kind of universal joint. The idea was that by tilting the movable head (when the pilot moved his control stick) the axis of rotation would be inclined slightly from the vertical, and thus its lift would pull slightly in that direction. However, there were problems when this system was used with the power-driven rotor of a helicopter, caused by the drive shaft as it rotated the tilted hub. When the hub was tilted the mass of the rotor was no longer "on center" over the shaft, and this caused serious vibration. Also, very great control forces were needed to move the rotor head.

The answer to this was the cyclic pitch control used on the majority of helicopters today. It had been discovered that you could get the same effect as rocking the hub by increasing the pitch of the blades in cycles as they rotated. As each blade swept through its full 360-degree circle, it changed pitch cyclically—that is, it assumed a high pitch at one point in the disc and then assumed a low pitch as it moved around to the opposite position. As the pitch was increased or decreased, the blades rose or fell on their flapping hinges, thus inclining the disc slightly from its vertical axis (this has been described in greater detail in Chapter VIII). The effect was that the tip path of the blades, as the rotor whirled around, was very much the same as it would have been with a rocking head rotor inclined in that direction.

What made this approach particularly attractive was that at the time of this experimentation, many rotating-wing aircraft, helicopters and rotorplanes alike, were already furnished with collective pitch control. This was a system for changing the pitch on all blades to the same degree, simultaneously, in order to take off vertically, and the blades were therefore mounted on bearings so they could be moved for pitch control along the span-wise axis. All that was needed was the mechanical system for controlling the pitch of the blades cyclically as well as collectively.

The device in a helicopter control system which accomplishes this, feeding the cyclic control movements to the rotor hub, is known by the rather interesting name of "swash plate." It is a doughnut-shaped unit that fits around the mast, actually consisting of two plates—an upper one and a lower one—with a bearing between the two. The upper plate is connected to the rotor hub by rods and consequently it spins around on the bearing as the rotor turns. The lower plate is linked to the pilot's cyclic control stick system and does not rotate. However this lower plate is mounted on pivots—either a spherical bearing or a gimbal ring—so that it can be tilted in any direction. As it tilts, the upper plate (which is moving in company with the hub) will be tilted as well. This results in a constant up and down movement in the link rods which connect the upper plate to the hub, accomplishing the cyclic pitch changes in the blades as they sweep around, and thus transmitting the pilot's control movements to the rotor.

While it is not intended here to delve too deeply into the design of the cyclic control system, there is another factor which should be considered, since it helps explain the workings of the linkage from the swash plate to the rotor hub. This is called the "90-degree phase lag" or time lag. When the pitch of a rotor blade is increased, the blade does not immediately rise but has to rotate for approximately another 90 degrees (a quarter of a revolution) before it reaches the highest flapped position; thus, there is a lag of approximately 90 degrees, attributed to blade inertia and gyroscopic factors, between the point at which the pitch is increased or decreased and the point where the full effect registers on the blade. Most helicopters have the control linkage from the swash plate to the hub offset by approximately 90 degrees to compensate for this; the pitch change is fed into the rotor at a point one-quarter of a revolution early in the plane of rotation. For example, when the pilot pushes the cyclic control stick forward so as to incline the rotor forward, as each blade comes around it will receive the decrease in pitch at the 90-degree point on the right (advancing) side and the increase in pitch at the opposite point on the left (retreating) side. Because of the time lag, each blade is in its highest flapped position directly over the tail of the helicopter and its lowest flapped position directly over the nose. This, of course, inclines the rotor disc forward as desired to propel the helicopter into forward flight.

In connection with the design of cyclic systems, one vital consideration is that the forces and loads acting on the tip of the blade are hundreds of times greater than the control forces which can be transmitted from the hub to the blade. The tip is going to go where it pleases, and the hub must be designed either to provide it with mechanical freedom through the use of hinges or, through structural flexibility, to move as it must under its dynamic loads. Even the so-called rigid rotor tends to behave like an articulated rotor because of the bending of the blades. (A blade rigid enough to resist these forces would be too heavy to fly.)

There is one important structural rigidity, however, that is essential to the correct functioning of a cyclic control system. The blade must be constructed so that it will not twist when pitch changes are made at the hub; it must have what a designer calls "torsional rigidity." If the blade failed to have this stiffness it would not be possible to transmit the pitch changes from the hub along the span of the blade out to the tip. Nevertheless, as with many of the basic concepts in rotor design, there are exceptions to this rule. One important example is the torsionally flexible blade used on some helicopters. With this system a type of pitch control is used that requires a blade that is deliberately flexible in torsion. On these rotors the pitch control is accomplished by actually warping the blades through the leverage obtained from a small, controllable, aerodynamic surface mounted on the trailing edge of the blade, similar to the trim tab used on airplane control surfaces.

Appendix

The Naming of the Helicopter

Few machines have had as many different names as the helicopter. Leonardo da Vinci, in writing of his proposal for a flying machine, called it only an "instrument" and a "screw," but in the second half of the eighteenth century, with a revival of interest in the idea of airscrew flight, a whole new family of words were created.

In 1754 the Russian scientist Lomonosov demonstrated a spring-driven model helicopter; in the English translation the name of this little machine reads "Aerodynamic." Fourteen years later (1768) a French mathematician, J. P. Paucton, described a man-powered helicopter which he called a "Pterophore." Another French name for an airscrew machine that appeared later in the eighteenth century (1784) was "Automoteur."

Still more words of French origin followed, indicating the steady interest in the subject in that country. "Automate" was coined in 1816 and "Aeroveliero" in 1823, but neither was widely accepted. Two words did catch on during the first half of the nineteenth century in France and were used to describe the popular toy helicopters, variations on the ancient Chinese top: "Spiralifere" and "Stropheor." The Spiralifere was a tiny rotor made of cardboard; when spun with a string it could rise a few yards into the air. The Stropheor was a more rugged version of the same toy; one contemporary writer said it was "much smaller and heavier [than the Spiralifere] and has sharp metal blades dangerous to passerby and attains the height of the most elevated belfries. . . ." In one form or another, the Stropheor was used by many of the nineteenth-century researchers to determine elementary rotor data. With only the short hops of this simple device as a basis, many overly enthusiastic experimenters predicted unbelievable performance for their full-scale designs.

On the whole, less imagination in creating new names was shown by the English-speaking inventors of the day; perhaps the language was less suited for concocting new and colorful variations. Sir George Cayley, simply called his rotating-wing aircraft "aerial carriage" or "aerial vehicle" (1843). In the United States, the magazine *Scientific American* described, in 1848, what seems to have been the first recorded design for a helicopter in this country—without giving any sort of name at all. The rotors, however, were called "wheel wings." a not inappropriate description. Another phrase used by an American inventor in 1869 was "aerial car"—a catch-all phrase comparable to "flying machine" and probably the least inspired of the lot.

Eventually, the French enthusiasm for creating new names paid off handsomely. In 1863 or thereabouts the Viscomte de Ponton d'Amecourt arrived at the name we use today. A dedicated advocate of rotating-wing flight, the viscount acted in company with other like-minded Parisians to speed its development, and he accomplished as much as could be done, considering the technology of his day (a 4-pound steam-driven coaxial model of his design is in the French Air Museum). His new word, based on the Greek "helicos" meaning *helix* and "pteron" meaning wing, was "Helicoptere." It soon caught on and was accepted in England and the United States as well, though in the English form the last "e" was dropped.

During the last half of the nineteenth century the word was often used with the limited meaning of "rotor" alone, for example as in "the flying machine was designed to be lifted by four helicopters." This is not surprising; after all, the only helicopters then flying were the tiny toy rotors made after the fashion of the Chinese top. Nevertheless, the word was safely installed in the dictionary, and when the first man-carrying helicopters appeared, after the turn of the new century, it was ready and waiting—one of the few cases in history where the name for a new machine existed before the fully developed invention itself.

Some inventors, naturally enough, were not eager to surrender the right to name their new creations, and any number of new words blossomed forth. The dean of the European inventors, Louis Bréguet, who test-hopped a four-rotor machine at Douai, France, in 1907 and then went on to build the first really successful European helicopter in 1935, insisted on the name "Gyroplane." This caused some confusion, since "Gyroplane" in the period before World War II was used regularly for still another form of rotating-wing aircraft, special types of rotorplanes similar to the Autogiro. Other names that appear in the record include "Aeromobile," "Autovol," and "Cyrnottero"—all dating from 1908, "Gyrocopter" (1910), "Gyroptere" (1915), "Alerion" (1919), "Helicogyre" (1920's), "Helicon" (1924), "Aerocar" (1931), and what was perhaps the prize of them all, the "Heliogyrocopter," also of 1931.

Angle of Attack

Angle of attack describes the small positive angle at which an airfoil (rotor blade or wing) meets the relative airflow; the leading edge of the airfoil is slightly higher, relative to the airflow from the front and below, than the trailing edge. Up to a certain critical angle, the lift force generated by the airfoil will increase as the angle of attack increases. If the angle of attack is raised beyond this critical point, the lift force will then start to fall off—at this point the airfoil is beginning to stall. For a typical rotor blade, this critical angle is approximately 14 degrees.

Pitch Angle

Pitch angle refers to the angle of the rotor blade airfoil to the horizontal (the vertical axis of the rotor mast is used as a reference point to establish the horizontal plane). This angle provides the bite of the blade into the airflow; it is variable and can be changed by movement of the pilot's controls. Ordinarily, the pitch angle is positive—that is, the leading edge of the blade is higher than its trailing edge.

It is sometimes thought that the pitch angle is the same as the angle of attack of the blade as it meets the airflow. In a very general way this is true, since the rotor obviously creates its own airflow by turning about the mast, and the angle of the blades, of course, is the angle at which they meet this horizontal flow. However, this is an incorrect oversimplification. The angle of attack of an airfoil is always considered in terms of the relative airflow, and the movement of the helicopter through the air will affect this flow. For example, when the aircraft is descending, there is airflow coming up through the rotor from beneath.

Blade Stall

A stall is a condition in which the airfoil (the wing of an airplane or the rotor blade of a helicopter) ceases to provide sufficient lift to maintain the aircraft in flight. Generally, a stall will result from the following interrelated causes: (1) insufficient airspeed, (2) too great an angle of attack, or (3) interference with the flow of air over the airfoil.

An example of a "normal" stall in a small airplane might be described in these terms. The pilot gradually eases back on his control stick, pulling the nose up, and thus drags the wings through the air at a higher and higher angle of attack. When a very high angle of attack is reached, ordinarily about 15 degrees or more, the air no longer flows smoothly over the top of the wing, the drag increases, and the lift force decreases. At some point, especially if the airflow is further disturbed by a slight turn or if the angle of attack is increased even more, the lift force produced by the wing will be less than the weight of the plane and the aircraft will begin to descend. This is the stall. Ordinarily, airplanes are designed so that, when a stall occurs, the machine will automatically go into a shallow dive to pick up airspeed; recovery can then be made easily.

In the case of a helicopter, stalling is something quite different. There is a condition (termed "blade stall") in which each blade can stall for an instant as it turns through one part of the disc of rotation and yet remain unstalled while rotating through the remainder of the disc area. With an airplane a stall usually occurs because the aircraft is flying too slowly, but with a helicopter, paradoxically, blade stall happens because the machine and its rotor system are moving through the air too fast. As was noted in the explanation of lift dissymmetry given in Chapter VIII, when the helicopter is in forward flight each blade reaches a point on one side of the disc where it is "retreating" from the airflow coming from the front, with a corresponding decrease in its relative airspeed and its lift. As the helicopter flies through the air at normal forward speeds, this effect is compensated for by the flapping action of the hinges at the hub, which increases the angle of attack—and therefore the lift—at that point.

If this concept can be grasped, it is clear that the faster the helicopter moves through the air in forward flight the worse the effect must be on the retreating blade and the greater the flapping action to increase the angle of attack. (It should be noted that only the tip section of the retreating blade is providing lift, since the airflow over the inner section is actually in a *reverse* direction.) Eventually, as the helicopter speeds up, the retreating blade reaches a condition where its angle of attack at the outer end of the blade exceeds the stalling angle. The result is that the airflow is disrupted and a "blade stall" occurs over that portion of the rotor disc. The stall is accompanied by excessive vibration; control problems as the aircraft tends to roll to one side; and by a considerable increase in drag—much added power and thrust is needed (such as direct-thrust jet engines) if the machine is to be flown any faster. Thus, blade stall is one of the critical factors tending to limit the top speed of any conventional helicopter.

Rotor Decay

A rotor blade depends upon the centrifugal force generated by its rotational speed (number of revolutions per minute) to maintain its correct coning angle and stiffness while in flight. If the rotor is allowed to slow down sufficiently the centrifugal force will decrease, with the unhappy result that the rotor blades may ride higher and higher until they fold upward entirely; at this point, needless to say, the helicopter will stop flying. This is rotor decay, the falling off or decay in the number of revolutions per minute. Obviously, the results of rotor decay can be unpleasant and permanent, but this phenomenon does not represent anything like a constant hazard; it occurs only when the rotor controls are grossly mismanaged, usually when the pitch is increased to an angle that is too great for the power available and the rotor is forced to slow down. A red line is marked on the pilot's tachometer to indicate the minimum allowable safe rotor speed.

Translation Lift

The term "translational lift" refers to the additional lift a helicopter gains as it moves from hovering into forward flight. To some extent, the rotor disc—the circular area swept by the blades—will behave as if it were a solid wing, picking up added lift over that created by the rotation of the blades. Because of the translational effect, the pilot actually has to reduce power slightly as he moves into forward flight; if he fails to do this, the aircraft may begin to climb. Helicopters, therefore, are the only type of aircraft in which the pilot actually *reduces* power as he speeds up.

Caliber

The word "caliber" is used to categorize firearms of different sizes. Ordinarily, the caliber is the dimension measured across the inside diameter of a gun barrel. It also refers to the thickness of the projectile fired from the gun, which of course fits tightly in the barrel and has the same dimension. For example, a .50-caliber machine gun fires a bullet that is fifty one-hundredths (one-half) inch in diameter. It is generally—though not always—true that the larger the caliber, the larger is the weapon and therefore the greater its range and destructive power. It should be noted that the dimension mentioned in Chapter V for a rocket projectile (2.75 inch) is the same kind of measurement as caliber: it refers to a rocket with a warhead that is two and three-quarters of an inch in diameter.

Bibliography

THE PUBLICATIONS listed here are credited as primary sources from which the book has been prepared. Although only a partial listing, these representative sources should be helpful to those interested in further research.

Books

Canby, Courtlandt, *A History of Flight*. New York: Hawthorn Books, 1963.

Cierva, Juan de la, and Don Rose, *Wings of Tomorrow*. New York: Brewer, Warren & Putnam, 1931.

Davy, M. J. B., *Interpretive History of Flight*. (Ministry of Education Science Museum) London: His Majesty's Stationery Office, 1948.

Francis, Devon Earl, *The Story of the Helicopter*. New York: Coward-McCann, 1946.

General View of Japanese Military Aircraft in the Pacific War.—compiled by the staff of *Aireview*. Tokyo: Kantosha Co., Ltd., 1956.

Hubler, Richard G., *Straight Up: The Story of Vertical Flight*. New York: Duell, Sloan & Pearce, 1961.

Karman, Theodore von, *Aerodynamics*. New York: McGraw-Hill, 1963.

Liberatore, Eugene K., *The Rotary Wing Industry*. Washington: U.S. Department of Commerce, Office of Technical Services, 1954.

Michelet, Guy, *Breguet*. Paris: Editions France-Empire, 1963.

Montross, Lynn, *Cavalry of the Sky*. New York: Harper & Brothers, 1954.

Morris, C. L., *Pioneering the Helicopter*. New York: McGraw-Hill, 1945.

Politella, Dario, *Operation Grasshopper*. Wichita: Robert R. Longo Co., 1958.

Pritchard, J. Laurence, *Sir George Cayley, the Inventor of the Airplane.* New York: Horizon Press, 1962.

Richards, Denis, and Hilary St. George Saunders, *Royal Air Force 1939-1945.* London: Her Majesty's Stationery Office, 1953.

Shapiro, Jacob, *The Helicopter.* New York: Macmillan, 1960.

Shirer, William L., *The Rise and Fall of the Third Reich.* New York: Simon and Schuster, 1960.

Sikorsky, Igor S., *The Story of the Winged-S.* New York: Dodd, Mead, 1958.

Swanborough, F. G., *Vertical Flight Aircraft of the World.* London: Temple Press Books, 1964.

Sykes, Christopher, *Orde Wingate, a Biography.* Cleveland: World Publishing Co., 1959.

Taylor, John W. R., *A Picture History of Flight.* New York: Pitman Publishing Corp., 1956.

Turner, Charles C., *Aerial Navigation of Today.* London: Seeley & Co., Ltd., 1910.

United States Air Force, Headquarters Air Force ROTC, *Foundations of Airpower.* Washington: U.S. Government Printing Office, 1958.

Vandegrift, John L., Jr., *A History of the Air Rescue Service.* U.S. Air Force, Orlando Air Force Base, Florida: Rollins Press, 1959.

Articles

"Aircraft for the U.S. Army." *Shell Aviation News,* Shell Oil Company, London. (January, 1961, No. 271).

"Air Show Rescue—Wilmington, N.C." *Kaman Rotor Tips,* Kaman Aircraft Corporation, Bloomfield, Conn. (December, 1961, Vol. II, No. 6).

"Army Aviation Operation in Vietnam" by Lt. Col. Thomas J. Sabiston. *U.S. Army Aviation Digest,* Fort Rucker, Ala. (January, 1963, Vol. 9, No. 1).

"The Army Aviation Story, Part IX, Medical Evacuation" by Col. Spurgeon H. Neel and Major Roland H. Shamburek. *U. S. Army Aviation Digest,* Fort Rucker, Ala. (February, 1963, Vol. 9, No. 1).

"Army Continues Push For More Helicopters" by George C. Wilson. *Aviation Week and Space Technology,* McGraw-Hill, New York (November 30, 1964).

"Autogiro." *The New Yorker,* New York (November 1, 1930).

"Autogyros of Present and Past" by George Kurylenko. *Sport Aviation,* Official Publication of the Experimental Aircraft Association, Hales Corners, Wisconsin (June, 1961, Vol. 10, No. 6).

"The Bristol 171" by R. Hafner. *Journal of The Royal Aeronautical Society,* Royal Aeronautical Society, Lewis Press (Wightman & Co. Ltd.), London (April, 1949, Vol. 53, No. 469).

"British Rotorcraft" by Raoul Hafner. *Journal of the Royal Aeronautical Society,* Royal Aeronautical Society, London (Centenary Journal, 1866-1966, Volume 70, January 1966, Number 661).

"A Century of British Aeronautics—The Royal Aeronautical Society, 1866-1966" by J. Laurence Pritchard, Honorary Fellow, *Journal of the Royal Aeronautical Society*, London (Centenary Journal, 1866–1966, Volume 70, January 1966, Number 661).

"The Cierva Air Horse" by J. S. Shapiro. *Journal of the Royal Aeronautical Society*, Royal Aeronautical Society, Lewis Press (Wightman & Co., Ltd.), London (April, 1949, Vol. 53, No. 469).

"Copter Airlines Weather Storm" by James Woolsey, *American Aviation Daily*, published by the staff of *American Aviation Magazine*, American Aviation Publications, Washington (May 11, 1966, Vol. 1, No. 1).

"The Development of the Helicopter" by Peter W. Brooks. *World Helicopter and Vertical Flight*, Air Age Publications, Ltd., Bromley Kent, Great Britain (March, 1959, Vol. 2, No. 2).

"Domain of the Convertible Rotor" by R. Hafner. *Journal of Aircraft, American Institute of Aeronautics and Astronautics*, New York (November-December, 1964, Vol. 1, No. 6).

"The Fairey Gyrodyne" by J. A. J. Bennett. *Journal of the Royal Aeronautical Society*, The Royal Aeronautical Society, Lewis Press, Wightman & Co. Ltd., London (April, 1949, Vol. 53, No. 469).

"Fire Team Leader" by Captain Alan R. Todd, and other articles. *United States Army Aviation Digest*, Fort Rucker, Ala. (June, 1965, Vol. 11, No. 6).

"The Flettner Story—A Page from Helicopter History." *Flying Review International*, Purnell & Sons, Ltd., London (February, 1965, Vol. 20, No. 5).

"Four Kisses for a Copter Pilot" by Frank Delear, and other articles. *The Bee-Hive*, United Aircraft Corporation, East Hartford, Conn. January, 1959, Vol. XXXIV, No. 1).

"Future Combat 'Copter" and other articles. *Vertiflite—The Magazine of the American Helicopter Society*, New York (April, 1965, Vol. 11, No. 4).

"German Thinking on Rotary-wing Development" by Dr. E. H. Henrich Focke. *Journal of the Royal Aeronautical Society*, London (May, 1965, Vol. 69, No. 653).

"The Helicopter Roundtable" and other articles. *American Aviation*, American Aviation Publications, Washington (July, 1963).

"Helicopters and Heliports: At the Crossroads." *Flying*, Ziff-Davis, New York (February, 1964, Vol. 74, No. 2).

"Here Come the Convertiplanes" by Richard F. Dempewolff. *Popular Mechanics*, New York (June, 1954).

"His Air Commandos Used R-4's" *Sikorsky News*, Sikorsky Aircraft, Division of United Aircraft Corporation, Stratford, Conn. (March, 1966).

"History of the Autogiro" by George Townson, and other articles. *American Helicopter Society Newsletter*, New York (March, 1961, Vol. 11, No. 4).

"Link Luckett Awarded Carnegie Silver Medal" and other articles. *American Helicopter Society Newsletter*, New York (February, 1961, Vol. 7, No. 2).

"Mission" by Lieutenant Chadwick C. Payne, and other articles. *United States Army Aviation Digest,* Fort Rucker, Ala. (October, 1964, Vol. 10, No. 10).

"Ralph P. Alex Looks at Russian Aviation" by Ralph P. Alex. *American Helicopter Society Newsletter,* New York (July, 1959, Vol. 5, No. 7).

"Rotaries Remembered" by Norman Macmillan. *Shell Aviation News,* Shell Oil Company, London (1964, No. 312).

"Runway-Free Propulsion Systems of the Future" by Dr. W. C. J. Garrard. *Lockheed-Georgia Quarterly,* Lockheed Aircraft Corporation, Marietta, Ga. (Fall, 1963, Vol. 1, No. 1).

"Russia's Rapid Helicopter-Design Progress" by Eugene K. Liberatore. *Aviation Week and Space Technology,* McGraw-Hill, New York (February 27, 1956).

"Russia's Revelations" by the Technical Editor. *Royal Air Force Flying Review,* Royal Air Force Review Ltd., A Mercury House Publication, London (Summer, 1961, Vol. XVII, No. 1).

"Sikorsky's First Helicopter Flight" by Igor Sikorsky. *The Bee-Hive,* United Aircraft Corporation, East Hartford, Conn. (Spring, 1946, Vol. XXI, No. 2).

"Sikorsky's Other Sikorsky" by Natalie Mann, and other articles. *The Bee-Hive,* United Aircraft Corporation, East Hartford, Conn. (January, 1957, Vol. XXXII, No. 1).

"Soviet Vertical Flight Designs Keep Pace With West" by Eugene K. Liberatore. *Aviation Week and Space Technology,* McGraw-Hill, New York (March 5, 1956).

"Special Report—Army Aviation" and other articles. *Flying,* Ziff-Davis, New York (May, 1962, Vol. 70, No. 2).

"Special V/STOL Directory Issue." *Flying Review International,* Purnell & Sons, Ltd., London (November, 1963, Vol. 19, No. 2).

"Status of V/STOL Research and Development in the United States" by John P. Campbell. *Journal of Aircraft, American Institute of Aeronautics and Astronautics,* New York (May-June, 1964, Vol. 1, No. 3).

"Turbocopter Airliners Take Over" by E. H. Pickering, and other articles. *Flight Magazine,* Air Review Publishing, Dallas (December, 1962, Vol. 51, No. 12).

"Up-Down, the Plight of the Helicopter Airlines" by Captain Leslie G. Carter. *The Airline Pilot,* published by the Air Line Pilots Association, Chicago (June, 1965, Vol. 34, No. 6).

"V/STOL: A Special Report" and other articles. *American Aviation,* American Aviation Publications, Washington (March, 1965).

"V/STOL Special Report—How Soon the Breakthrough?" by Charles Giebelhaus. *Business/Commercial Aviation,* Conover-Mast, New York (August, 1962).

Reports, Booklets, and Other Sources

Army Aviation in the Field Army, FY-1963. U.S. Army Aviation School, Fort Rucker, Ala. (organizational training manual).

British Intelligence Objectives Sub-Committee Overall Report No. 8, Rotating Wing Activities in Germany during the period 1939-1945 by Captain R. N. Liptrot. Her Majesty's Stationery Office, London, 1948.

Conference on V/STOL Aircraft, a Compilation of the Papers Presented. National Aeronautics and Space Administration, Langley Field, Va., November 17-18, 1960.

Development of the Helicopter. Reprinted from the Spring, 1965, issue of *Lockheed Horizons,* Lockheed-California Company, Division of Lockheed Aircraft Corporation (historical booklet).

One Way Up by John F. Straubel. Hiller Aircraft Company, 1964 (historical booklet).

Preliminary Study of V/STOL Transport Aircraft and Bibliography of NASA Research in the VTOL/STOL Field. National Aeronautics and Space Administration, D-624, Langley Field, Va., January, 1961.

Prelude to Kitty Hawk by Walter T. Bonney. Historical reprint in one volume from *The Pegasus,* published by the Fairchild Engine and Aircraft Corporation, 1953.

Sikorsky Helicopter Flight Theory for Pilots and Mechanics by John R. Montgomery. Sikorsky Aircraft, Division of United Aircraft Corporation, Stratford, Conn., 1964.

The Miracle of the Helicopter by Frank J. Delear. Sikorsky Aircraft, Division of United Aircraft Corp., Stratford, Conn., 1963 (revised).

Picture Credits

24: The Smithsonian Institution, negative no. A-47937-K
25: From *British Intelligence Objectives Sub-Committee Overall Report No. 8, Rotating Wing Activities in Germany during the period 1939-1945*, reproduction by courtesy of the Controller of Her Britannic Majesty's Stationery Office
26: Societe des Ateliers d'Aviation Louis Breguet
27: Eugene K. Liberatore
28: Sikorsky Aircraft, Division of United Aircraft Corporation
29: From *British Intelligence Objectives Sub-Committee Overall Report No. 8, Rotating Wing Activities in Germany during the period 1939-1945*, reproduction by courtesy of the Controller of Her Britannic Majesty's Stationery Office
30: From *British Intelligence Objectives Sub-Committee Overall Report No. 8, Rotating Wing Activities in Germany during the period 1939-1945*, reproduction by courtesy of the Controller of Her Britannic Majesty's Stationery Office
31: Eugene K. Liberatore
32: Sikorsky Aircraft, Division of United Aircraft Corporation
33: U.S. Air Force Photo
34: U.S. Information Agency, Photo no. 306-NT-1276-8 in the National Archives
35: Wide World Photos
36: Bell Helicopter Company
37: From *One Way Up*, a publication of the Hiller Aircraft Company
38: Sikorsky Aircraft, Division of United Aircraft Corporation
39: Sikorsky Aircraft, Division of United Aircraft Corporation
40: From *One Way Up*, a publication of the Hiller Aircraft Company
41: U.S. Army Photograph
42: De Lackner Helicopters, Inc., Mount Vernon, N.Y.
43: Sikorsky Aircraft, Division of United Aircraft Corporation
44: U.S. Air Force Photo
45: U.S. Air Force Photo
46: Sikorsky Aircraft, Division of United Aircraft Corporation
47: From *One Way Up*, a publication of the Hiller Aircraft Corporation
48: U.S. Air Force Photo
49: From *A History of the Air Rescue Service*, 1959, by John L. Vandegrift
50: Kaman Aircraft Corporation
51: American Helicopter Society
52: U.S. Army Photograph
53: *Life* Magazine ©1965 Time Inc. All Rights Reserved
54: Defense Department Photo, Marine Corps
55: U.S. Army Photo
56: Wide World Photos
57: Bell Aircraft Corporation

58: Adapted from the Lockheed-Georgia *Quarterly*
59: Societe des Ateliers d'Aviation Louis Breguet
60: Convertawing, Inc.
61: Bell Aircraft Corporation, reproduction by U.S. Army
62: Hiller Aircraft Company
63: Hawker Siddeley Aviation, Ltd.
64: Sikorsky Aircraft, Division of United Aircraft Corporation
65: From the old *Life* magazine, March 4, 1909
66: Museum of Modern Art Film Library
67: British European Airways
68: Sikorsky Aircraft, Division of United Aircraft Corporation
69: Boeing Photo (Vertol Division/Boeing)
70: *N.Y. Daily News* Photo
71: Eastern Air Lines
72: Hughes Tool Company, Aircraft Division
73: Sud-Aviation Corporation
74: Sikorsky Aircraft, Division of United Aircraft Corporation
75: Hughes Tool Company, Aircraft Division
76: Charles Gablehouse
77: U.S. Navy
78: Charles Gablehouse
79: Adapted from a drawing furnished by Eugene K. Liberatore
80: U.S. Navy
81: Hughes Tool Company, Aircraft Division

Index